70037210

D0188558

OCR

AS

Revise

Physics

Exclusively endorsed by OCR for GCE Physics A

Second
Edition

David Sang

www.heinemann.co.uk

✓ Free online support
✓ Useful weblinks
✓ 24 hour online ordering

01865 888080

In Exclusive Partnership

TROWBRIDGE
LEARNING CENTRE

Heinemann is an imprint of Pearson Education Limited, a company
incorporated in England and Wales, having its registered office at Edinburgh
Gate, Harlow, Essex, CM20 2JE. Registered company number: 872828

www.heinemann.co.uk

Heinemann is a registered trademark of Pearson Education Limited

Text © David Sang 2008

First published 2000
This edition 2008

12 11 10 09 08
10 9 8 7 6 5 4 3 2 1

British Library Cataloguing in Publication Data is available from the British
Library on request

ISBN 978 0 435583 72 9

All rights reserved. No part of this publication may be reproduced in any form
or by any means (including photocopying or storing it in any medium by
electronic means and whether or not transiently or incidentally to some other
use of this publication) without the written permission of the copyright owner,
except in accordance with the provisions of the Copyright, Designs and Patents
Act 1988 or under the terms of a licence issued by the Copyright Licensing
Agency, Saffron House, 6–10 Kirby Street, London EC1N 8TS (www.cla.co.uk).
Applications for the copyright owner's written permission should be addressed
to the publisher.

Edited by Melanie Thompson
Designed by Wearset Ltd, Boldon, Tyne and Wear
Project managed and typeset by Wearset Ltd, Boldon, Tyne and Wear
Illustrated by Wearset Ltd, Boldon, Tyne and Wear
Cover photo © Science Photo Library
Printed in the UK by Ashford Colour Press Ltd

Acknowledgement
We would like to thank Harvey Cole for his invaluable help in reviewing this
book.

Contents

Introduction

How to use this revision guide

This revision guide is for the OCR Physics AS course. It is divided into two units to match Specification A. You may be taking a test at the end of each unit, or you may take all of the tests at the end of the course. The content is exactly the same.

Each unit begins with an **introduction** that summarises the content. It also reminds you of the topics from your GCSE course that the unit draws on.

The content of each unit is presented in **modules**, to help you divide your study into manageable chunks. Each module is dealt with in one or more spreads. These do the following:

- They **summarise** the content.
- They indicate **points to note**.
- They include **worked examples** of calculations.
- They include **diagrams** of the sort you might need to reproduce in tests.
- They provide **quick check** questions to help you test your understanding.

You can tackle the quick check questions as you work through the spread, or at the end of the spread. In the margin you will see markers to tell you at which point you have covered the necessary content to tackle each quick check question.

At the end of each unit, there are longer **end-of-unit questions** similar in style to those you will encounter in tests. **Answers** to all questions are provided at the end of the book.

You need to understand the **scheme of assessment** for your course. This is summarised on page v, opposite. At the end of the book, you will find a list of the various **formulae** and **definitions** you need to learn, and the others that are provided in tests.

A note about units

In the worked examples, we have included units throughout the calculations. (See, for example, the worked examples on pages 4 and 5.) This can help to ensure that you end up with the correct units in your final answer. See also the note on checking units on page 7.

In tests, it is not necessary to include units in intermediate steps in calculations.

OCR AS Physics – Assessment

There are three **units of assessment** (1, 2 and 3) in this AS Physics course. There are no optional units.

- Units 1 and 2 are externally assessed (by tests).
- Unit 3 includes assessment of **experimental skills** and is internally assessed.

The A2 course is divided into three units in a similar way, with similar weightings.

Unit	OCR Code	Name	Duration of written test	Marks available	Weighting
1	G481	Mechanics	1 hour	60	30%
2	G482	Electrons, waves and photons	1 hour 45 minutes	100	50%
3	G483	Practical skills in Physics 1	1 hour	40	20%

In Unit 3, the practical tasks are set by OCR and marked within your centre, using a mark scheme provided by OCR.

Question types

There are no optional questions in the test papers – you have to answer all the questions.

- The questions are **structured questions** that require brief answers to several linked parts of a question.
- Parts of some questions require **extended answers**. These are used to assess the quality of your **written communication**.

Use the mark allocation and the space available for your answer to guide how much you write.

About the tests

- **Written tests** will be available in January and June.
- **Practical tests** are only available in June.
- **Re-sits** may be taken as often as you wish; the best result counts, so you cannot end up with a lower score.
- **Aggregation** means combining the scores for each unit of assessment. You may enter for aggregation at the end of the AS course, or carry your marks forward to the A2 year.
- AS units have half the **weighting** indicated above when they are carried over to the full Advanced GCE award. So AS counts for 50% of A-level.

A companion revision guide is available in this series for the A2 part of the course.

Examiner tip

As a guide, in the test papers for G481 and G482 you should work a little faster than one mark per minute, so a nine-mark question should take no more than about 9 minutes.

UNIT 1

Mechanics

To help you organise your learning, each unit of the specification is broken down into modules. There are three modules in this unit.

- **Module 1: Motion** considers how we can describe the motion of an object in terms of displacement, velocity, acceleration and time. It also looks at the difference between vector and scalar quantities and how vector quantities can be combined.

- **Module 2: Forces in action** brings in the idea of forces and how they affect an object's motion. Newton's laws of motion relate force to acceleration. An object falling under gravity is accelerated; the drag force of air resistance changes as the object accelerates. Understanding how forces affect objects can help to understand safety features of vehicles. This module also looks at the turning effect of a force.

- **Module 3: Work and energy** extends ideas about forces to work, energy and power. Calculations of these quantities can predict what will happen when two objects interact. This module also looks at how forces deform materials.

This unit counts for 30% of the AS qualification.

Your practical classes will have prepared you for the assessment of practical skills (Unit G483; see page v). There are some experiments that you must be able to describe as part of unit 1 (G481) for the examination. These are:

- an experiment to determine the acceleration of free fall, g, by studying a falling body (page 12)

- an experiment to determine the centre of gravity of an object (page 19)

- an experiment to determine the Young modulus of a metal in the form of a wire (pages 26–27).

For each experiment, you should be able to:

- sketch the appropriate apparatus and label it

- describe the measurements you would make

- show how to calculate the result

- comment on possible sources of error and inaccuracy.

Module 1 – Motion, pages 2–13

Topic (in this book)	Reference to specification	Ideas from GCSE
Velocity and displacement	1.1.2a 1.1.3a, b, c, d, e	Relationship between speed, distance and time
Acceleration	1.1.3a, b, c, e, f	Graphical representation of speed, distance and time Acceleration as change in velocity per unit time
Equations of motion – parts 1 and 2	1.1.4a, b	
Using vectors	1.1.2b, c, d	
Gravity and motion	1.1.4c, d, e, f	Forces on a falling body

Module 2 – Forces in action, pages 14–21

Topic (in this book)	Reference to specification	Ideas from GCSE
Force, mass, acceleration	1.2.1a, b, c, d	Balanced forces do not alter velocity Quantitative relation between force, mass and acceleration
Gravity and weight	1.2.2a–g	Weight is the force of gravity on a body
Turning effect	1.2.3a–j	Principle of moments Pressure, force and area
Car safety	1.2.4a–f	Factors affecting stopping distances of vehicles

Module 3 – Work and energy, pages 22–27

Topic (in this book)	Reference to specification	Ideas from GCSE
Force, work, energy and power	1.3.1a–f 1.3.3a–f	Calculations of work and power
Kinetic and potential energy	1.3.2a–e	Calculations of changes between kinetic and potential energy
Deforming solids	1.3.4a–i	Stretching effect of a force

End-of-unit questions, pages 28–31

Velocity and displacement

Key words

- displacement
- speed
- velocity
- vector quantity
- scalar quantity

When an object moves, we may be able to describe its motion using a graph, or an equation. First, we need to define some basic terms.

Speed, distance, time

We can find the **average speed** of a moving object by measuring the distance it travels in an interval of time:

$$\text{average speed} = \frac{\text{distance travelled}}{\text{time taken}}$$

This equation defines average speed. It can only tell us the object's *average* speed; it may be speeding up or slowing down. An object's **instantaneous speed** is the rate at which the distance travelled is changing at a moment in time.

✓ *Quick check 1*

Motion in a straight line

If an object is moving at a steady speed in a straight line, it is in *uniform motion*. Two quantities describe its motion:

- **displacement** – the distance it has travelled in a particular direction;
- **velocity** – its speed in a particular direction.

These are related by the equation:

$$\text{velocity} = \frac{\text{displacement}}{\text{time}} \qquad v = \frac{s}{t}$$

This equation defines velocity. In words:

The velocity of an object is the rate of change of its displacement.

It is important to be able to rearrange the equation for velocity to make time or displacement the subject:

$$\text{displacement} = \text{velocity} \times \text{time} \quad s = vt$$

$$\text{time} = \frac{\text{displacement}}{\text{time}} \quad t = \frac{s}{v}$$

Hint

Take care! The symbol *s* is used for displacement, not speed. Do not confuse it with s for seconds.

SI units

In the international system of units (SI units), displacement or distance is measured in *metres* (m), time in *seconds* (s) and velocity in *metres per second* (m s⁻¹). You may come across velocities in a variety of units; keep an eye on the units of displacement and time:

$$\text{m s}^{-1} \qquad \text{mm s}^{-1} \qquad \text{km s}^{-1} \qquad \text{km h}^{-1}$$

Hint

See Appendix 2 on page 77 for more about SI units.

■ WORKED EXAMPLE

A car travels at 25 m s⁻¹ for 5 minutes due north along a straight road. What is its displacement after this time?

STEP 1 Write down what you know, and what you want to know:
velocity $v = 25$ m s⁻¹, time $t = 5$ min $= 300$ s, displacement $s = ?$

STEP 2 Choose the form of the equation with displacement as its subject:
displacement = velocity × time $s = vt$

STEP 3 Substitute values and solve:
$s = 25$ m s⁻¹ × 300 s $= 7500$ m $= 7.5$ km

So the car's displacement is 7.5 km due north. Note that, to give a complete answer, we have included the *direction* of the displacement.

✓ *Quick check 2, 3*

Examiner tip

Sometimes in an exam you will be asked to *define* a term or unit. You should learn these definitions of vector and scalar quantities and be able to give examples. See also pages 82–83.

Vector and scalar quantities

The definitions of displacement and velocity should remind you of the difference between vector and scalar quantities.

- A **vector quantity** has both magnitude (size) and direction (e.g. displacement, velocity).

- A **scalar quantity** has only magnitude (e.g. distance, speed).

Hint

More about the representation of vector quantities on page 10.

✓ *Quick check 4*

Displacement–time graphs

The shape of an object's displacement–time graph shows how its motion is changing. In this example,

1 a straight line sloping up shows that it is going away at a steady speed ('*positive* velocity')
2 a horizontal line shows that it is stationary for a while ('*zero* velocity')
3 a straight line sloping down shows that it is coming back at a steady speed ('*negative* velocity').

In the curved graph the object is speeding up (accelerating); its velocity is positive and increasing.

The *gradient* (slope) of the displacement–time graph is the velocity. Here, Δ (delta) just means 'change in', so Δs means 'change in displacement'.

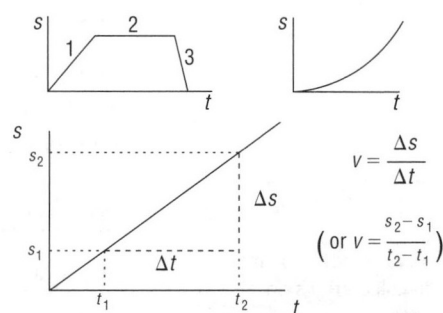

$$v = \frac{\Delta s}{\Delta t}$$

$$\left(\text{or } v = \frac{s_2 - s_1}{t_2 - t_1} \right)$$

Hint

Check that the y-axis shows displacement.

✓ *Quick check 5, 6*

QUICK CHECK QUESTIONS

1 A bus travels along its 20 km route in 40 minutes. Calculate its average speed, and explain why this is only an average.

2 A rocket rises 2000 m vertically upwards in 10 s. What is its average velocity?

3 How long will it take a car travelling at 30 m s⁻¹ to travel 1200 m?

4 A spacecraft orbits the Earth at a constant speed of 8 km s⁻¹. Explain whether its velocity is also constant.

5 Sketch a displacement–time graph to represent the motion of a car that is initially travelling at a steady speed, but suddenly comes to a halt.

6 The table below shows how the displacement of a runner along a straight track changes with time. Plot a displacement–time graph. Use it to find the runner's velocity during the first 10 s.

displacement (m)	0	45	90	130	172
time (s)	0	5	10	15	20

UNIT 1

Acceleration

Key words

- acceleraton
- velocity–time graph

An object is **accelerating** if it is speeding up, **decelerating** if it is slowing down. Its acceleration is a measure of how rapidly its velocity is changing.

Defining acceleration

The **acceleration** of an object is the rate of change of its velocity. If its velocity v changes by an amount Δv in a time interval Δt, its acceleration a is given by:

$$\text{acceleration} = \frac{\text{change in velocity}}{\text{time taken}} \qquad a = \frac{\Delta v}{\Delta t}$$

We can write this in a different way:

$$\text{acceleration} = \frac{\text{final velocity} - \text{initial velocity}}{\text{time}} \qquad a = \frac{v - u}{t}$$

We need different symbols for initial velocity and final velocity. Remember that u comes before v, so u represents initial velocity.

Hint

Here, Δ (delta) does not represent a quantity. It stands for 'a change in'. So Δv means 'change in velocity'.

Units

Acceleration is almost always given in m s^{-2} (metres per second squared). It can help to think of an acceleration of, say, 10 m s^{-2} as an increase in velocity of 10 m s^{-1} every second.

Signs

An object with a *negative* acceleration is slowing down (this is sometimes referred to as a deceleration or retardation). An object with *zero* acceleration either has uniform velocity (steady speed) or is stationary. *Positive* acceleration means speeding up.

Hint

See the note on units in calculations on page iv.

✔ *Quick check 1, 2*

■ WORKED EXAMPLE

A car accelerates from 10 m s^{-1} to 18 m s^{-1} in 4 s. What is its acceleration?

STEP 1 Write down what you know, and what you want to know:
$$u = 10 \text{ m s}^{-1}, v = 18 \text{ m s}^{-1}, t = 4 \text{ s}, a = ?$$
STEP 2 Write down the equation, substitute and solve:
$$a = \frac{v - u}{t} = \frac{18 \text{ m s}^{-1} - 10 \text{ m s}^{-1}}{4 \text{ s}} = \frac{8 \text{ m s}^{-1}}{4 \text{ s}} = 2 \text{ m s}^{-2}$$

Typical values

It is useful to remember the following values.

Hint

The acceleration in free fall is called g – see page 12.

- The acceleration in free fall is about 10 m s^{-2} (in fact, the average value of g on Earth is 9.81 m s^{-2}).
- The acceleration of a car or person is usually no more than 2 or 3 m s^{-2}, as in the worked example.
- Even a jet aircraft taking off usually has an acceleration of less than 10 m s^{-2}.

Velocity–time graphs

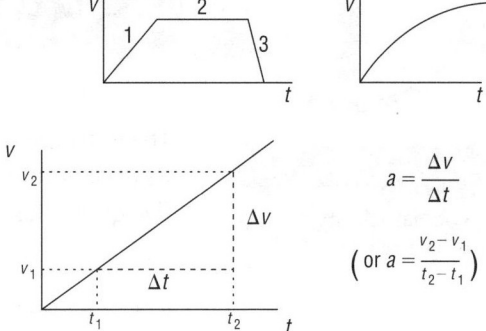

Just as we can draw a displacement–time graph (see page 3), we can draw a velocity–time graph to show how an object's *velocity* is changing. In the first graph,

1 a straight line sloping up indicates steadily *increasing* speed (uniform *'positive'* acceleration)
2 a horizontal line shows steady speed (*'zero'* acceleration)
3 a straight line sloping down shows steadily *decreasing* speed (*'negative'* acceleration, or deceleration).

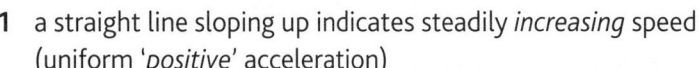

$$a = \frac{\Delta v}{\Delta t}$$

$$\left(\text{or } a = \frac{v_2 - v_1}{t_2 - t_1} \right)$$

The gradient (slope) of the velocity–time graph is the acceleration.

To find the acceleration at any instant, find the gradient of the tangent to the curve.

The curved graph with decreasing gradient shows decreasing acceleration.

The area under the velocity–time graph gives the displacement, because it is the average speed multiplied by the travelling time (see page 6).

✓ *Quick check 3*

Module 1

Examiner tip

Always check the label on the *y*-axis – does the graph show displacement or velocity?

■ WORKED EXAMPLE

Find the displacement after 50 s of the object whose velocity–time graph is shown in the diagram.

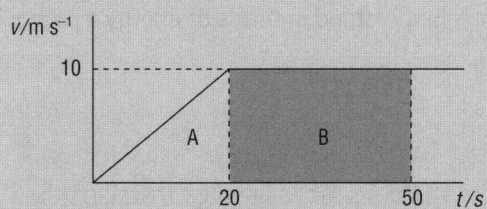

Examiner tip

Include all the steps in your working. Even if your final answer is wrong, you may gain some credit for part of an answer.

STEP 1 Divide the area under the graph into a triangle and a rectangle.
STEP 2 Calculate the area of each part – see graph.

> **Triangle A:** $\frac{1}{2}$ **base × height** = $\frac{1}{2}$ × 20 s × 10 m s⁻¹ = 100 m.
> **Rectangle B:** 30 s × 10 m s⁻¹ = 300 m.

STEP 3 Add these together to give total displacement = 400 m.

✓ *Quick check 4*

QUICK CHECK QUESTIONS

1 An aircraft accelerates from 200 m s⁻¹ to 300 m s⁻¹ in 25 s. What is its acceleration?
2 A car has an acceleration of 8 m s⁻². How long will it take to reach a speed of 24 m s⁻¹, starting from rest?
3 Sketch a velocity–time graph for a car that is initially travelling with constant velocity and which then decelerates to a halt at a steady rate.
4 A train travels at a steady speed of 30 m s⁻¹ for 100 s. As it approaches a station, it decelerates at a steady rate so that it comes to a halt after 50 s. Draw a velocity–time graph for the train's motion, and use it to calculate:
 a the train's acceleration as it slows down
 b the total distance travelled during the time described.

Hint

You will have to rearrange the equation for acceleration. Alternatively, think of the acceleration as '8 m s⁻¹ every second'.

Equations of motion – part 1

Key words

- initial velocity
- final velocity

The *equations of motion* can be used when an object is accelerating at a steady rate, i.e. its acceleration a is constant. There are *five* equations that need to be learnt. They link five quantities:

u initial velocity v final velocity s displacement
a acceleration t time

The five equations

Here are the five equations. Note that each equation involves four of the five quantities. The worked example includes brief comments; more comments are given with the derivations on pages 8–9.

Hint

These equations only apply to an object moving with uniform (constant) acceleration, and in a straight line.

1   $v = u + at$ Does not involve s. A rearrangement of $a = \dfrac{v-u}{t}$ (see page 4)

2   $s = \dfrac{v+u}{2} \times t$ Does not involve a. Says displacement = average velocity × time

3   $s = ut + \dfrac{1}{2}at^2$ Does not involve v. With zero acceleration, becomes displacement = velocity × time

4   $s = vt - \dfrac{1}{2}at^2$ Does not involve u.

✔ *Quick check 1*

5   $v^2 = u^2 + 2as$ Does not involve t. Easier to understand in terms of energy and work – see page 16

Examiner tip

In rough calculations, you may find it easier to omit the units; however, they provide a check that the quantities are correct. In examinations, the unit may be included in the answer line, e.g. speed = ... m s⁻¹. If the unit is given, make sure it matches your calculation, e.g. you might do a calculation giving an answer in cm, when the answer line requires an answer in m.

■ **WORKED EXAMPLE 1**

A car travelling at $20\ \mathrm{m\ s^{-1}}$ accelerates at $2\ \mathrm{m\ s^{-2}}$ for 5 s. How far will it travel in this time?

STEP 1 Write down what you know, and what you want to know:
$u = 20\ \mathrm{m\ s^{-1}},\ t = 5\ \mathrm{s},\ a = 2\ \mathrm{m\ s^{-2}},\ s = ?$

STEP 2 Choose the appropriate equation linking these quantities:
$$s = ut + \frac{1}{2}at^2$$

STEP 3 Substitute and solve.
$$s = [20\ \mathrm{m\ s^{-1}} \times 5\ \mathrm{s}] + \left[\frac{1}{2} \times 2\ \mathrm{m\ s^{-2}} \times (5\ \mathrm{s})^2\right]$$
$$= 100\ \mathrm{m} + 25\ \mathrm{m} = 125\ \mathrm{m}$$

Notice that the car's displacement is made up of two parts: 100 m is the distance it would have travelled in 5 s at a steady $20\ \mathrm{m\ s^{-1}}$; 25 m is the extra distance travelled because it is accelerating.

■ WORKED EXAMPLE 2

For the car in worked example **1**, use equation 4 to find the car's velocity after it has travelled 125 m (after 5 s). Then use equation 1 to check your answer.

STEP 1 Write down what you know, and what you want to know:
$u = 20$ m s^{-1}, $a = 2$ m s^{-2}, $s = 125$ m (from worked example 1), $v = ?$

STEP 2 Choose the appropriate equation linking these quantities. The question requires equation 4:
$v^2 = u^2 + 2as$

STEP 3 Substitute and solve.
$v^2 = (20$ m s$^{-1})^2 + 2 \times 2$ m s$^{-2} \times 125$ m
$= 400$ m^2 s$^{-2} + 500$ m^2 s$^{-2} = 900$ m^2 s^{-2}
$v = \sqrt{900}$ m^2 s$^{-2} = 30$ m s^{-1}

STEP 4 Check using equation 1 ($t = 5$ s).
$v = u + at = 20$ m s$^{-1} + 2$ m s$^{-2} \times 5$ s $= 30$ m s^{-1}

Hint

Here you are told which equation to use, but this will not usually be the case – you will have to select the appropriate equation.

Hint

Note that it is necessary to start a new line when changing from v^2 to v.

✓*Quick check 2–6*

Checking units

In each of the equations of motion, the units on either side must be the same. For example, take the third equation:

$s = ut + \dfrac{1}{2}at^2$

On the left-hand side, we have a single term (s, displacement); the units of displacement are metres (m).

On the right-hand side, we have two terms added together; each must have units of m:

First term ut: units are m s$^{-1} \times$ s = m (because s^{-1} and s cancel).

Second term $\dfrac{1}{2}at^2$: units are m s$^{-2} \times$ s^2 = m (because s^{-2} and s^2 cancel).

✓*Quick check 7*

QUICK CHECK QUESTIONS

1 An aircraft accelerates at a steady rate from 200 m s^{-1} to 300 m s^{-1} in 80 s. Calculate its acceleration in this time, and its average speed.

2 A stone drops from rest with an acceleration of 9.81 m s^{-2}. How far will it fall in 2.0 s?

3 A skier moving at a steady speed of 15 m s^{-1} reaches a steeper slope where her acceleration is 1.25 m s^{-2}. How fast will she be travelling after she has moved 160 m from the top of the slope?

4 A train travelling at 10 m s^{-1} accelerates steadily. After 45 s it has reached a speed of 14 m s^{-1}. How far does it travel in this time?

5 At the start of a race, a runner accelerates from rest with a uniform acceleration of 4.5 m s^{-2} for 1.8 s. How fast will she be moving after this time?

6 At a motorway exit, a truck driver brakes from 30 m s^{-1} to 12 m s^{-1} with a deceleration of 2 m s^{-2}. For how long and over what distance is he braking?

7 For each of the equations of motion, give the units of each term.

Hint

'From rest' tells you that its initial velocity was zero.

Hint

Here a is negative.

UNIT 1

Equations of motion – part 2

There are five equations of motion (see page 6). The first two come from the definitions of velocity and acceleration. The other three can be derived from the first two. This shows that the equations are not independent of one another.

To understand how the equations of motion are related to one another, it is best to start from a graph that represents uniformly accelerated motion. The graph is a straight line. We will also use the following ideas (from pages 4–5):

- acceleration is the *gradient* of the velocity–time graph
- displacement is the *area* under the velocity–time graph.

Equation 1: *v = u + at*

The gradient of the graph is the acceleration. Hence we can write

$$a = \frac{v-u}{t}$$

Rearranging gives $at = v - u$, and hence

$$v = u + at$$

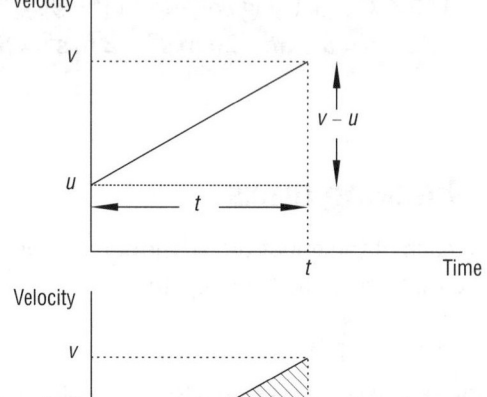

Equation 2: $s = \frac{v+u}{2} \times t$

The average velocity is the average of

v and u, i.e. $\frac{v+u}{2}$

This is shown by the *dashed* line in the diagram.

The distance travelled is the average velocity × time taken. Hence

$$s = \frac{v+u}{2} \times t$$

✔*Quick check 1*

This is the rectangular area under the dashed line and is the same as the area under the sloping line.

Equation 3: deriving $s = ut + \frac{1}{2}at^2$

We start from equations 1 and 2:

$$v = u + at \text{ and } s = \frac{v+u}{2} \times t$$

We want a new expression for *s*. Using equation 1, we substitute for *v* in equation 2:

$$s = \frac{u+at+u}{2} \times t = \frac{2u+at}{2} \times t$$

Multiplying out gives $s = \frac{2u}{2} \times t + \frac{at}{2} \times t$

and simplifying gives $s = ut + \frac{1}{2}at^2$

Alternative derivation

This is the same graph as before. The area under the graph is the displacement, and is made up of two parts: a rectangle and a triangle.

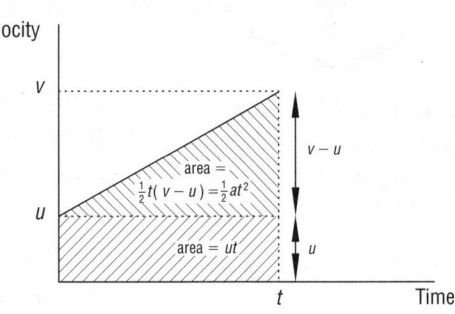

The rectangle represents the displacement of an object moving with velocity u for time t:

Area of rectangle = width × height = ut

The triangle represents the extra distance travelled because the object is speeding up:

Area of triangle = $\dfrac{1}{2}$ base × height = $\dfrac{1}{2}t \times (v - u)$

From $a = (v - u)/t$ we can say that $v - u = at$, so:

Area of triangle = $\dfrac{1}{2}t \times (v - u) = \dfrac{1}{2}t \times at = \dfrac{1}{2}at^2$

Adding the two areas gives the total displacement:

$$s = ut + \frac{1}{2}at^2$$

✓*Quick check 2*

Equation 4: deriving $s = vt - \dfrac{1}{2}at^2$

We start from equations 1 and 2

$$v = u + at \quad \text{and} \quad s = \frac{v + u}{2} \times t$$

Using equation 1, we substitute for u in equation 2

$$s = \frac{v + (v - at)}{2} \times t = \frac{2v - at}{2} \times t$$

which gives $s = \dfrac{2v}{2} \times t - \dfrac{at}{2} \times t$, simplified to $s = vt - \dfrac{1}{2}at^2$

✓*Quick check 3*

Equation 5: deriving $v^2 = u^2 + 2as$

Starting from $v = u + at$, we have $v - u = at$.

Starting from $s = \dfrac{v + u}{2} \times t$, we have $v + u = \dfrac{2s}{t}$

Multiplying these two equations together gives

$$(v + u) \times (v - u) = \frac{2s}{t} \times at = 2as$$

The left-hand side is the difference of two squares, i.e. $v^2 - u^2$. So $v^2 - u^2 = 2as$ and rearranging gives $v^2 = u^2 + 2as$.

QUICK CHECK QUESTIONS

1 Car A is travelling at a steady speed of 15 m s^{-1}. It overtakes car B, which is travelling at 10 m s^{-1}. Car B's driver immediately starts to accelerate uniformly. Car B catches up with car A after 20 s. *On the same axes*, draw velocity–time graphs to represent the motion of the two cars. What is car B's speed when it catches up with car A? Use your graph to show that the cars travel 300 m before B catches up with A.

2 A car, initially travelling at 7 m s^{-1}, accelerates steadily for 10 s until it reaches a speed of 12 m s^{-1}. Draw a velocity–time graph to represent this motion. Use the graph to deduce the car's acceleration, and how far it travels.

3 A spacecraft travelling in a straight line accelerates from 8 km s^{-1} to 12 km s^{-1} with an acceleration of 1.6 km s^{-2}. How far does it travel whilst accelerating?

Hint

You will have to rearrange $v^2 = u^2 + 2as$

Hint

Check your answer using $s = \dfrac{v + u}{2} \times t$

Using vectors

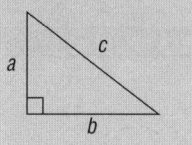

Key words

- magnitude
- direction
- resolving
- components

Hint

Reminder of Pythagoras' theorem: for a right-angled triangle, $a^2 + b^2 = c^2$.

Hint

You can think of this as 'Going from A to B to C is the same as going directly from A to C'.

✓ *Quick check 1*

Examiner tip

In an examination you may sketch the triangle and use Pythagoras and trigonometry **or** you may use a scale drawing and measure v and θ. Choose a suitable scale, e.g. 1 cm = 1 m s^{-1}. Make sure you have a ruler and protractor with you!

Hint

It is always advisable to check a calculation like this by drawing a scale diagram and measuring both the length of the resultant and the angle.

✓ *Quick check 2*

Vector quantities, such as displacement, velocity and acceleration, have both *magnitude* and *direction*. They cannot simply be represented by a numerical value. Instead, to include their direction, they can be represented by drawing *vector diagrams*. In a vector diagram:

- the *length* of a line represents the magnitude of the vector quantity
- the *direction* of a line represents the direction of the vector quantity.

Vector diagrams are a type of scale drawing.

Adding two vectors

Draw a *vector triangle* as follows.

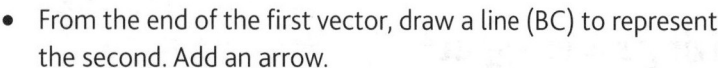

- Choose a suitable scale. Draw a line (AB) to represent the first vector quantity. Add an arrow to the line.

- From the end of the first vector, draw a line (BC) to represent the second. Add an arrow.

- Return to the *start* of the first vector. Draw a line from this point to the *end* of the second vector. This line (AC) represents the *resultant* of the two. Add *two* arrowheads to show that this is the resultant of the other two vectors. This process is called *adding two vectors*.

When the two vectors are perpendicular, the triangle is right-angled and the resultant is the hypotenuse. Use Pythagoras' theorem to calculate the resultant.

■ **WORKED EXAMPLE**

A ship is sailing due north at 8 m s^{-1}. A passenger walks across the deck at 4 m s^{-1}, in an easterly direction. What is her resultant velocity?

The diagram shows how the two velocities are added.

STEP 1 Draw a vector to represent the velocity of the ship.
STEP 2 Draw a vector to represent the passenger's velocity across the deck.
STEP 3 Draw the resultant vector.
STEP 4 Measure or calculate the resultant. In this case, we have a right-angled triangle, so we can calculate the resultant using Pythagoras' theorem.

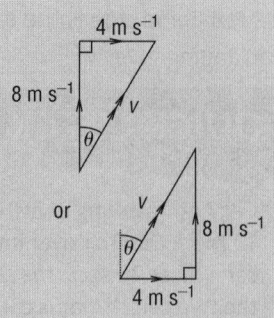

$$v^2 = (8 \text{ m s}^{-1})^2 + (4 \text{ m s}^{-1})^2 = (64 + 16) \text{ m}^2 \text{ s}^{-2}$$
$$= 80 \text{ m}^2 \text{ s}^{-2}$$
$$v = \sqrt{80 \text{ m}^2 \text{ s}^{-2}} = 8.9 \text{ m s}^{-1}$$

We must also state the *direction* of the passenger's resultant velocity. We need to find the angle θ from the diagram.

$$\tan \theta = \frac{\text{opp}}{\text{adj}} = 4/8 = 0.5$$

$$\theta = \tan^{-1} 0.5 = 26.6°$$

The passenger's resultant velocity is thus 8.9 m s^{-1} at 26.6° east of north.

Resolving a vector

Sometimes it is useful to **resolve** (break down) a vector quantity into two **components** at 90° to one another.

Imagine turning the vector V round to point in the direction of interest. If you turn the vector through an angle θ, the component of V in this direction is $V \cos \theta$.

A vector may be replaced by two perpendicular components whose values are $V \cos \theta$ and $V \sin \theta$. Notice that if these two components are *added* (see page 10), the resultant is the original vector.

The *perpendicular components* of a vector are *independent* of one another. Changing one component has no effect on the other.

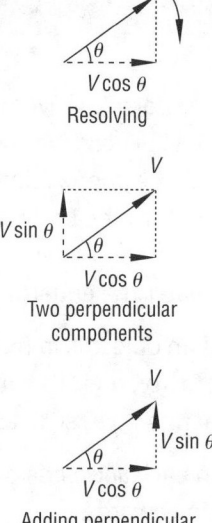

Resolving

Two perpendicular components

Adding perpendicular components

✓ *Quick check 3*

■ WORKED EXAMPLE

A car is travelling at 20 m s⁻¹ at 30° W of N (see diagram). Calculate the components of its velocity due N and due W.

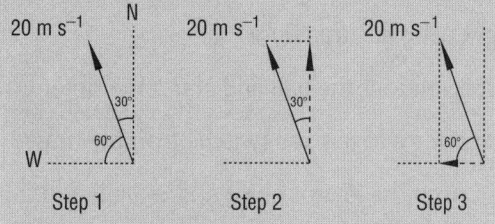

Step 1   Step 2   Step 3

STEP 1 Draw a diagram; mark the relevant angles.
STEP 2 Calculate the component due N. (The angle here is 30°.)
    Component due N = 20 m s⁻¹ × cos 30° = 17.3 m s⁻¹
STEP 3 Calculate the component due W. (The angle here is 60°.)
    Component due W = 20 m s⁻¹ × cos 60° = 10.0 m s⁻¹

Hint

Note that we could have calculated this last result using sin 30° rather than cos 60°.

✓ *Quick check 4*

QUICK CHECK QUESTIONS

1 A plane flies NE for 200 km, then due E for 400 km. Draw a scale diagram of its journey and use it to deduce its distance from the starting point.

2 A whale swims 1000 km due S and then 400 km due E. How far is it from its starting point, and in what direction?

3 The Earth's gravity makes objects fall with an acceleration of $g = 9.81$ m s⁻². What will be the acceleration of an object down a smooth slope, inclined at 45° to the horizontal?

4 A boy is speeding at 8 m s⁻¹ down a water slide which is inclined at 35° to the horizontal. Calculate the horizontal and vertical components of his velocity.

Hint

Calculate the component of g at 45° to the horizontal.

UNIT 1

Gravity and motion

Key words
- free fall
- projectile

The Earth's gravitational pull causes objects to accelerate as they fall. For objects near the surface of the Earth, the acceleration caused by gravity has the *approximate* value $g = 9.81$ m s^{-2}. This decreases the further you go from the Earth's centre, so the value of g varies over the Earth's surface. It is greater nearer the poles where the Earth is slightly flattened, and less nearer the equator, as well as at higher altitudes.

$t = 0$
$t = 1$ s
$t = 2$ s

If an object is in **free fall**, this means that the only force acting on it is gravity; therefore its acceleration is equal to g. If there is another force acting on it, such as air resistance, its acceleration will be different from g.

In each succeeding second, the object falls further. It is accelerating downwards.

$t = 3$ s

Acceleration of free fall $g = 9.81$ m s^{-2}.

Quick check 1–3

For an object falling vertically under the effect of gravity (and no other force), you can use the equations of motion (pages 6–9) because the object has constant acceleration.

Measuring g

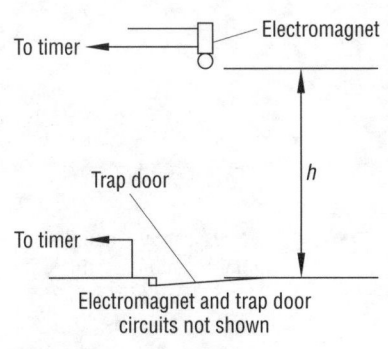

To timer — Electromagnet

Trap door

h

To timer

Electromagnet and trap door circuits not shown

Quick check 4

A steel ball is held by an electromagnet above a trap door.

The electromagnet is switched off; this releases the ball and starts the timer.

The ball falls through the trap door, breaking a circuit and switching off the timer.

From the distance fallen h (measured from the lowest point on the ball) and the time taken, the acceleration can be calculated: $h = \frac{1}{2} g t^2$.

Sources of error: it may be difficult to measure t accurately. There may be a delay between switching off the current and the ball being released. Similarly, there may be a delay between the ball striking the trap door and the circuit breaking. Air resistance should be negligible.

Projectile motion

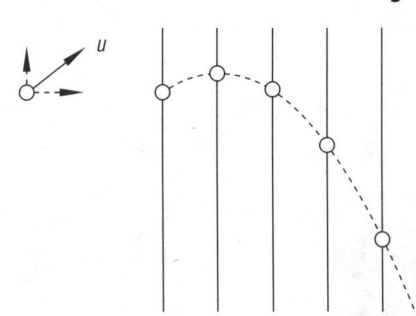

u

An object thrown in any direction except vertical follows a curved (parabolic) path through the air. Gravity acts on it vertically, and it has no horizontal acceleration.

- Horizontal motion: constant velocity.
- Vertical motion: uniform acceleration g.

The diagram represents a ball moving freely under gravity. It has been projected at an angle to the horizontal, and its position is shown at equal intervals of time. Here we are assuming that air resistance is negligible, so that the only force acting is gravity.

- Horizontal motion: the positions are equally spaced, showing that it moves equal distances in equal times.
- Vertical motion: the spacing of the images increases as the ball falls, showing that it is accelerating downwards.

To solve problems, resolve the initial velocity into horizontal and vertical components and treat them separately.

■ WORKED EXAMPLE

A ball is projected horizontally with an initial velocity of 2.0 m s⁻¹. It reaches the ground, a distance of 5.0 m below. Calculate the time taken and the horizontal distance it travels.

STEP 1 Find the components of its initial velocity. In this case, this is simple because it is moving horizontally at the start.

Horizontal component of u = 2.0 m s⁻¹
Vertical component of u = 0 m s⁻¹

STEP 2 Consider the ball's vertical motion, as this determines how long it takes to reach the ground. We know:

Initial velocity u = 0 m s⁻¹
acceleration a = 9.81 m s⁻²
displacement s = 5.0 m

STEP 3 Choose the appropriate equation of motion, substitute values and solve:

$s = ut + \frac{1}{2}at^2$
$5.0 = 0 + 0.5 \times 9.81t^2$
$t^2 = 5.0/(0.5 \times 9.81) = 1.02$
$t = 1.01\ s$

Hence the ball lands after 1.01 s

STEP 4 Now calculate the horizontal distance travelled in this time.

Distance = speed × time = 2.0 m s⁻¹ × 1.01 s = 2.02 m

✓ *Quick check 5*

Galileo and Aristotle

Before the sixteenth century, there was a very different idea of the way in which objects moved. These ideas, derived from Aristotle, suggested that:

- An object has an inherent tendency to reach as low a point as possible.

- A moving object comes to a halt when the 'force' that started it moving 'runs out'.

(This is not like our current idea of force; it is more like the idea of momentum.)

So the Aristotelian idea of a projectile was that it travelled along until it ran out of force; then it fell to the ground. Galileo performed experiments which showed that this was not a good explanation of observations. He learned to time things, and to measure the paths of moving objects. He made objects move on sloping ramps, rather than vertically, as this has the effect of 'diluting' gravity so that motion can be more clearly seen.

He showed that, in equal intervals of time, a projectile moved equal distances horizontally but increasing distances vertically.

> **Examiner tip**
>
> This is not included just out of historical interest – you may be asked examination questions on it!

QUICK CHECK QUESTIONS

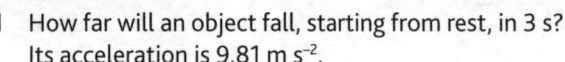

1 How far will an object fall, starting from rest, in 3 s? Its acceleration is 9.81 m s⁻².

2 The acceleration of free fall on the surface of Mars is 3.8 m s⁻². On Mars, how far will an object fall, starting from rest, in 3 s?

3 A body falling vertically through air experiences air resistance (drag). This force increases as the body speeds up. Explain why you could not use the equations of motion in such a circumstance.

4 In the experiment to determine g, there may be a delay in the ball being released when the electromagnet is switched off. If the timer responds instantaneously, how will this affect the values of t and g?

5 A stone is projected from level ground with an initial velocity of 5.0 m s⁻¹ at an angle of 45° above the horizontal. How long will it take to return to the ground, and how far will it travel?

> **Hint**
>
> When the stone lands, its vertical displacement $s = 0$.

Force, mass, acceleration

Key words

- force
- unbalanced
- newton
- fundamental unit
- derived unit

So far, we have only *described* motion. Now we can go on to use the idea of forces to *explain* why motion changes. Newton's laws of motion tell us about how forces change motion:

- If the forces on an object are *balanced*, it will remain at rest or continue to move with constant velocity (i.e. at a steady speed in a straight line).
- If the forces on an object are *unbalanced*, its motion will change; it will accelerate in the direction of the unbalanced force.

Force and acceleration

Force, mass and acceleration are related by the equation:

force = mass × acceleration $F = ma$

Here, F is the *unbalanced force* (the resultant force) in newtons (N) acting on an object of mass m in kilograms (kg). It gives the object an acceleration a in m s^{-2} *in the direction of the force*. See 'Units: the newton' on page 15.

The equation $F = ma$ is often used as a shorthand way of remembering Newton's second law of motion, but don't forget that *direction* is important too.

To sum up, an object acted on by an unbalanced force will accelerate. Its acceleration is proportional to the force and is in the direction of the force.

✓Quick check 1

■ WORKED EXAMPLE

A car of mass 1000 kg is acted on by two forces: a forward force of 500 N provided by its engine, and a retarding (backward) force of 200 N caused by air resistance. What is its acceleration?

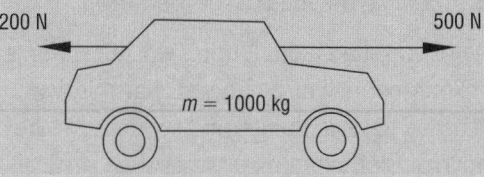

200 N   500 N $m = 1000$ kg

STEP 1 Draw a diagram to show the forces acting on the car. (It can help to draw a longer arrow for the larger force.)

STEP 2 Calculate the unbalanced force and note its direction.
$F = 500\ N - 200\ N = 300\ N$ **forwards**

STEP 3 Calculate the acceleration by rearranging $F = ma$.

$$a = \frac{F}{m} = \frac{300\ N}{1000\ kg} = \frac{300\ kg\ m\ s^{-2}}{1000\ kg} = 0.3\ m\ s^{-2}$$

So the car's acceleration is 0.3 m s^{-2} forwards.

Hint

Don't forget to state the direction.

✓Quick check 2–4

Units: the newton

The unit of force is the **newton**. The equation $F = ma$ defines the newton:

$$1\,N = 1\,kg \times 1\,m\,s^{-2}$$

A newton is the force that will give a mass of 1 kg an acceleration of 1 m s^{-2}. Equally, it will give a mass of 0.5 kg an acceleration of 2 m s^{-2}, and so on.

The kilogram, metre and second are **fundamental units** in the SI system. The newton is a **derived unit**. Most units we use are derived units; it is important to be able to trace them back to the fundamental units.

The meaning of mass

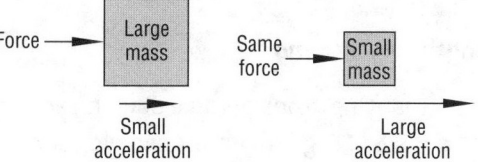

The equation $F = ma$ also tells us what we mean by '**mass**'. Imagine the same unbalanced force acting on two objects, one of large mass, the other of small mass. The object with larger mass will accelerate less than the object with smaller mass.

Mass is the property of an object that resists change in motion.

In diagrams, it often helps to label an object with its mass, but don't put an arrow. Mass does not have direction – it is a *scalar* quantity.

A note of caution: the equation $F = ma$ cannot be used for objects moving at very high speeds. This is because, according to Einstein's Special Theory of Relativity, an object's mass increases as it approaches the speed of light c. Hence, as the object accelerates, m increases and the equation is no longer appropriate.

Examiner tip

This is a definition. You may be asked to 'define the newton'.

Hint

More about the relationships between units in the SI system can be found in Appendix 2 on page 77.

Module 2

Hint

Don't confuse mass with weight – see page 16.

Hint

The speed of light in a vacuum, c, is close to 3.0×10^8 m s^{-1}.

✓ *Quick check 5, 6*

QUICK CHECK QUESTIONS

1. Is force a vector or a scalar quantity?

2. What force is needed to give a ball of mass 2.4 kg an acceleration of 15 m s^{-2}?

3. A parachutist of mass 80 kg and weight 800 N is acted on by an upward drag force of 960 N. What is her acceleration?

4. An object's mass can be measured by finding the acceleration produced when a known force acts on it. A force of 600 N gives a car an acceleration of 0.8 m s^{-2}. What is the car's mass?

5. Is mass a vector or a scalar quantity?

6. When force F acts on object A, the object is given an acceleration of 13 m s^{-2}. When the same force F acts on object B, its acceleration is 14 m s^{-2}. Which has the greater mass, A or B?

Hint

Don't forget to state its direction.

Gravity and weight

Key words

- weight
- mass
- drag
- terminal velocity
- air resistance

The Earth's gravitational pull on us causes us to have *weight*. This is a force that acts on us all the time, so that we hardly notice its existence. Because our weight is proportional to our *mass*, we tend to get the two ideas confused.

Calculating weight

The fact that a falling object accelerates shows that there must be an unbalanced force acting on it – its **weight**. An object's weight depends on two factors:

- its mass, m (the greater its mass, the greater its weight);
- the gravitational field strength, g.

> **weight = mass × gravitational field strength** $W = mg$

The **gravitational field strength** g tells you how many newtons of force pull on each kilogram of mass. It has the approximate value $g = 9.81$ N kg^{-1} (newtons per kilogram) near the Earth's surface.

The acceleration caused by gravity $g = 9.81$ m s^{-2} and the gravitational field strength $g = 9.81$ N kg^{-1} are two different ways of saying the same thing. 1 N kg^{-1} is the same as 1 m s^{-2}. On the surface of the Moon, gravity is much weaker. The field strength is 1.6 N kg^{-1}, so falling objects have an acceleration of 1.6 m s^{-2}.

Hence we can write:

> **weight = mass × acceleration of free fall** $W = mg$

✓ *Quick check 1–3*

Weight and mass

The weight of an object is the gravitational force acting on the object, measured in newtons. It is represented by an arrow. The weight of an object depends on where it is, because gravitational field strength varies from place to place.

✓ *Quick check 4*

Mass is a property of an object. It tells us how much matter it is made of. It is a measure of resistance to change in motion. It does not vary from place to place.

Falling through air

An object falling through air experiences air resistance, known as **drag**. This is a resistive force, opposing motion, and is always in the opposite direction to velocity. Drag depends on the surface area of an object; bigger objects experience greater drag. Air resistance increases as an object moves faster. Eventually, air resistance equals the object's weight, and the forces are balanced. The object cannot go any faster; it has reached **terminal velocity**.

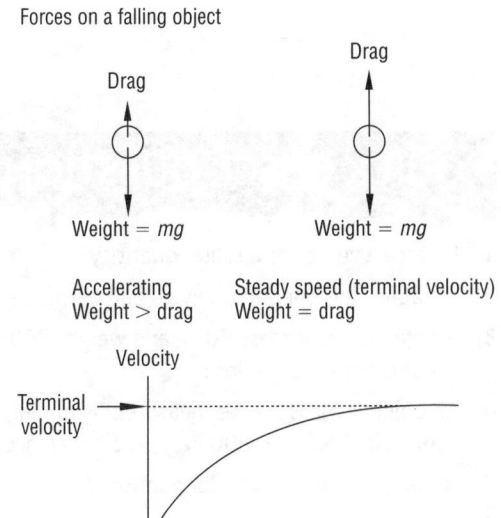

Forces on a falling object

Drag

Weight = mg

Accelerating
Weight > drag

Drag

Weight = mg

Steady speed (terminal velocity)
Weight = drag

Velocity

Terminal velocity

Time

✓ *Quick check 5*

This explains why cars, for example, have a top speed. The forward force of the engine is matched by the backward force of air resistance. To go faster, the car would need an engine that provided a greater force; alternatively, it could be redesigned to reduce air resistance.

■ WORKED EXAMPLE

A parachutist of mass 80 kg is falling through air. The force of air resistance on her is 1200 N. Calculate her acceleration.

STEP 1 Calculate the weight of the falling object.
weight = mg = 80 kg × 9.81 N kg^{-1} = 785 N

STEP 2 Draw a free-body force diagram for the object, and use it to calculate the resultant force acting on the object.
resultant force = 1200 − 785 = 415 N upwards

STEP 3 Calculate the acceleration using $F = ma$:

Acceleration $a = \dfrac{F}{m} = \dfrac{415\ \text{N}}{80\ \text{kg}} = 5.2\ \text{m s}^{-2}$ upwards

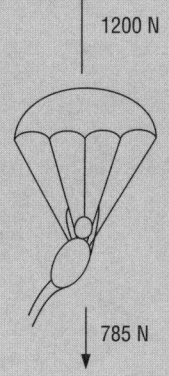

1200 N

785 N

Hint

The diagram will help you to see the direction of the resultant force. It helps to use a longer arrow to represent the larger force.

✓ *Quick check 6*

Examiner tip

It is important that you do not give too many (or too few) significant figures (sf) in your final answer. Here, the data in the question is given to 2 sf, so the answer is given to 2 sf. Usually, 2 or 3 sf will be acceptable.

QUICK CHECK QUESTIONS

1 What is the weight of a person of mass 40 kg on the Earth's surface?

2 A rock weighs 480 N on the Earth's surface. What is its mass?

3 The gravitational field strength on the surface of Mars is 3.8 N kg^{-1}. What will an object of mass 60 kg weigh there?

4 Is weight a vector or a scalar quantity? Is mass a vector or a scalar quantity?

5 A skydiver is falling at a steady speed of 50 m s^{-1}. He opens his parachute so that the force of air resistance increases. Describe and explain how his motion will change after this.

6 A stone of mass 3.0 kg is falling with an acceleration of 4.0 m s^{-2}. Calculate the force of air resistance acting on it. Explain how the following quantities will change as the stone continues to fall: air resistance, resultant force, acceleration.

Turning effect

Key words

- moment
- torque
- equilibrium
- centre of gravity
- density
- pressure

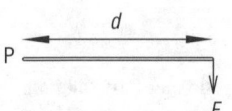

F and d perpendicular:
moment = $F \times d$

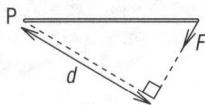

Draw a line from point P
at 90° to line of force:
moment = $F \times d$

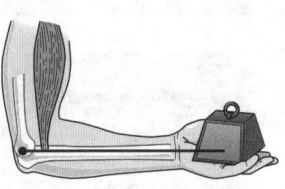

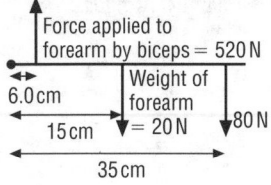

✓ *Quick check 1*

Forces can have many different effects on the objects they act on. The **moment** of a force tells us about its *turning effect*. The moment of a force about a point (the *pivot*) is defined as:

moment = *magnitude* of the force × perpendicular *distance* of its line of action from the pivot

It is important to be able to determine the distance between the point and the line of action (direction) of the force. The worked example illustrates another method.

Units: Moment is measured in **newton metres** (N m).

■ WORKED EXAMPLE

A force of 100 N acts at an angle of 30° to a beam, and at a distance $x = 4.0$ m from one end. What is the moment of the force about this end?

Method 1

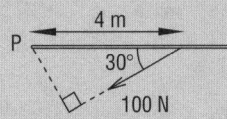

STEP 1 Draw the line of action of the force. Then draw a perpendicular line from P to the line of action.

STEP 2 Calculate the length d of this line:
$d = 4.0$ m × sin 30° = 2.0 m

STEP 3 Multiply by the force to find the moment:
moment = $F \times d$ = 100 N × 2.0 m = 200 N m

Method 2

STEP 1 Calculate the component of F perpendicular to x:
component of F = 100 N × cos 60° = 50 N

STEP 2 Calculate the moment of this component about P:
moment = 50 N × 4.0 m = 200 N m

Of course, both methods give the same answer.

Torque of a couple

A **couple** is a pair of forces. They are equal in magnitude, and act in opposite directions, but they do not lie in the same line. Because they are equal and opposite, they do not make the object accelerate away. However, because they do not line up, they tend to make the object *rotate*. The moment of a couple is its **torque** in N m.

torque of a couple = magnitude of one force × perpendicular distance between them

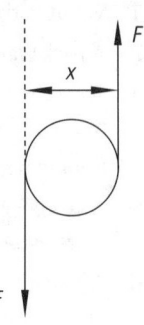

✓ *Quick check 2*

Equilibrium

If an object is **in equilibrium**, it will not accelerate, and it will not start to rotate. For this to happen:

- there must be no resultant (unbalanced) force acting on it;
- there must be no resultant torque acting on it.

Centre of gravity

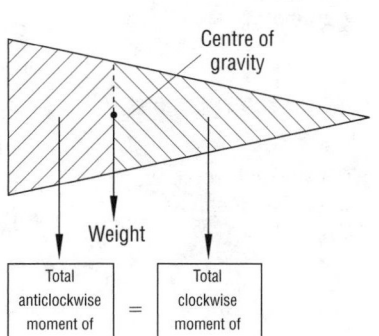

✔ *Quick check 3*

An object may have a complicated shape; gravity acts on all parts of it. Every object has a single point, called its **centre of gravity**, on each side of which the moments of all the separate parts of the object are balanced.

We can represent the weight of the whole object by a downward arrow acting at its centre of gravity. This greatly simplifies problem solving.

Experiment to find the centre of gravity of an object:

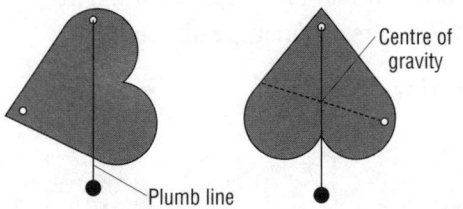

1 pivot object near one edge
2 draw vertical line on object through pivot
3 pivot object from second pivot point
4 draw vertical line from pivot
5 where the two lines cross is the centre of gravity.

Density

The **density** of a substance is its mass per unit volume, symbol ρ (Greek letter rho).

$$\rho = \frac{M}{V}$$

✔ *Quick check 4*

Pressure

Pressure is defined as force per unit area: $p = \frac{F}{A}$

It is measured in N m⁻², also known as *pascals* (Pa).

The greater the force and the smaller the area it acts on, the greater the pressure.

✔ *Quick check 5*

QUICK CHECK QUESTIONS

1 Calculate the moment about P of each of the two forces shown in the upper diagram.

2 Which two of the forces shown in the lower diagram constitute a couple? What is their torque?

3 Copy the diagram for question **2**. Add another force, acting at point X, which will leave the object in equilibrium. Show that there is no resultant force or torque acting on it.

4 What is the density of a substance if 24 kg occupies 0.04 m³? What volume would be occupied by 1200 kg of the substance?

5 The pressure of the atmosphere is 10⁵ Pa. What force does it exert on a box of surface area 1.5 m²?

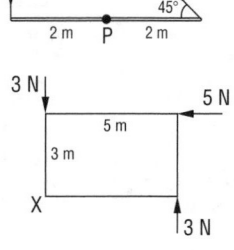

19

Car safety

An understanding of forces and motion can help to make cars and their drivers safer.

Key words

- thinking distance
- braking distance
- stopping distance
- crumple zone

Stopping distances

Picture a car travelling along a road. The driver notices something on the road ahead and decides to stop. Obviously, the faster the car is travelling, the longer it will take to come to a halt. But we can analyse this situation in more detail.

- Firstly, it takes a fraction of a second for the driver to react – this is the *thinking time*, in which the car travels a short distance called the **thinking distance**. If the car has been travelling at a steady speed, it will maintain that speed during this time. Calculate thinking time using $s = ut$.

- Then, once the brakes are applied, the car travels a further distance called the **braking distance** before coming to a halt. During this time, it is decelerating. Use $v^2 = u^2 + 2as$ to calculate the stopping distance, where v = final speed = zero.

stopping distance = thinking distance + braking distance

Hint

Thinking time for an alert driver is about 0.7 s.

✔ *Quick check 1*

■ WORKED EXAMPLE

A car is travelling at a steady speed of 20 m s⁻¹. The driver sees an obstruction on the road ahead, and applies the brakes after a thinking time of 0.7 s. The car slows down with an acceleration of −4.0 m s⁻². Calculate the stopping distance.

STEP 1 Calculate the thinking distance:
  Thinking distance = thinking time × speed = 0.7 × 20 = 14 m
STEP 2 Calculate the braking distance using $v^2 = u^2 + 2as$:

$$s = \frac{20^2}{2 \times 4.0} = 50 \text{ m}$$

STEP 3 Calculate the total stopping distance:
  Stopping distance = 14 m + 50 m = 64 m

✔ *Quick check 2, 3*

Factors affecting stopping distance

Different factors affect thinking distance and braking distance.

Thinking distance depends on speed and thinking time.

- The greater the vehicle's speed, the greater the thinking distance.
- Thinking time increases with age (reactions are slower), and also if the driver is under the influence of drugs (alcohol, recreational, medical), or is tired.

Braking distance depends on the speed at which the vehicle is travelling, and the acceleration with which it slows down.

- Because the distance travelled while braking depends on the square of the speed (u^2), double the speed gives four times the braking distance.
- If the car's tyres are bald, and if the road surface is smooth or wet, friction (and hence deceleration) will be reduced and the braking distance will be greater.

✔ *Quick check 4*

Safety features

When a car comes rapidly to a halt, for example in a crash, it is important that the occupants of the car are brought to a halt as gently as possible. This means that the time taken for them to come to a halt must be as long as possible. Several features help to protect the occupants:

The **crumple zones** are less-rigid structures at the front and back of the car. They are crushed in an impact, so that the force of impact is not transferred directly to the occupants (who are protected in a rigid steel 'cage').

Seat belts and air bags bring the driver gradually to rest, avoiding a sudden sharp impact with the windscreen or dashboard. The release of an air bag is triggered by an accelerometer, a tiny electronic device that responds to the vehicle's sudden, large deceleration in an impact. An explosive charge is set off, exploding the bag outwards towards the driver (see illustration, right).

GPS satellite navigation systems help drivers to find their way around. The receiver picks up signals from at least three satellites; it then calculates the distances from the satellites and deduces the car's position on the Earth's surface. This is *trilateration*.

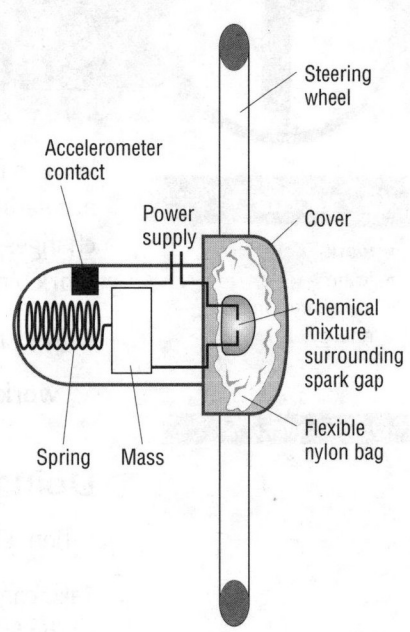

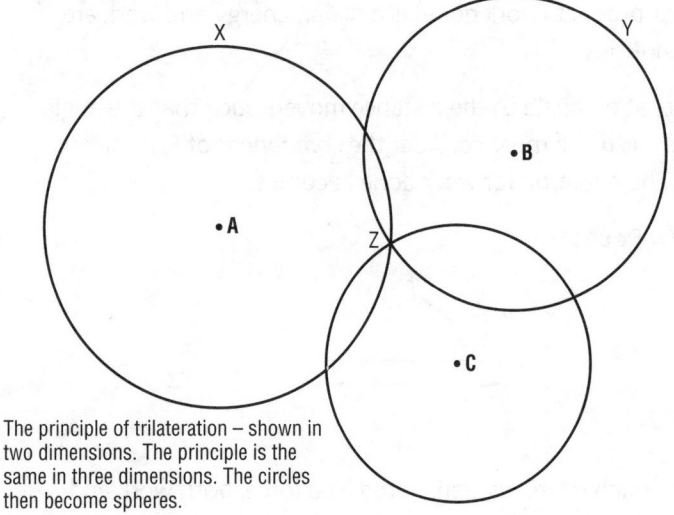

The principle of trilateration – shown in two dimensions. The principle is the same in three dimensions. The circles then become spheres.

Module 2

✓ *Quick check 5*

Examiner tip

If you are asked to explain how air bags, seat belts etc. protect a driver, do not write vague statements about 'cushioning'. Time to stop is longer, so deceleration is less, so from $F = ma$, F is less.

QUICK CHECK QUESTIONS

1 A car is travelling at 22 m s⁻¹. How far will it travel at this speed during a thinking time of 0.75 s?

2 What will be the braking distance for a car travelling at 12 m s⁻¹ if it decelerates at 1.5 m s⁻²?

3 A driver travelling at 15 m s⁻¹ sees an obstruction ahead. She reacts quickly and applies the brakes after 0.6 s. The car decelerates to rest at 3 m s⁻². Calculate the thinking distance, braking distance and stopping distance.

4 A driver is travelling on an icy road. Explain why he or she should travel more slowly in such circumstances. Your answer should refer to stopping distance.

5 Why is it important that a seat belt should have a certain amount of 'give' in it?

Force, work, energy and power

Key words

- work
- joule
- conservation of energy

✓ *Quick check 1*

We use forces to do things – to start things moving, to make them accelerate or decelerate, to change their shape. When a force changes the *energy* of something in this way, we say that it does **work**. Energy has been *transferred*.

Gravity pulls you straight down: $W = Fx$

work done = energy transferred

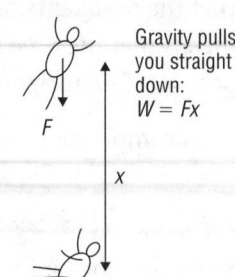

Gravity pulls you straight down: $W = Fx$

Doing work

When a force F pushes an object for a distance x, the work W done by the force is Fx.

Take care when using $W = Fx$! The displacement x must be measured along the direction of the force.

work done = force × displacement *in the direction of the force* $W = Fx$

Although both force and displacement in a particular direction are vector quantities, their product (work done) is a scalar. Energy and work are both scalar quantities.

Gravity pulls you down the slope, but the displacement in the direction of the force is x, not y; $W = Fx$

✓ *Quick check 2, 3*

If the force acts at an angle to the distance moved, such that the angle between F and x is θ, we must consider the *component* of F in the direction of x. The equation for work done becomes:

work done $W = Fx \cos \theta$

Defining the joule

Since work done tells us how much energy is transferred by a force, both work and energy are measured in the same units, called **joules** (J). The equation $W = Fx$ relates joules to newtons and metres.

1 joule = 1 newton × 1 metre; 1 J = 1 N m

1 joule is the energy transferred when a force of 1 newton moves through 1 metre. Equally, it is the energy transferred when a force of 0.5 N moves through 2 m, and so on. So, in fundamental units, $1\,J = 1\,N\,m = 1\,kg\,m\,s^{-2}\,m = 1\,kg\,m^2\,s^{-2}$.

✓ *Quick check 4*

Energy conservation

Energy can take many different forms – thermal (heat), kinetic, gravitational potential, etc. It can be changed from one form to another, but the total amount always remains constant. This is the *principle of conservation of energy*:

In a closed system, the total amount of energy remains constant.

This is represented in a *Sankey diagram* on the next page. The total width of the arrow remains constant, but it divides to show the proportions which change from one form to another.

Although energy cannot be created or destroyed, it can be wasted. In other words, when we change energy from one form to another, some may 'escape' in a form that we do not require and cannot use. (Usually this is heat, often it is sound.) The efficiency of an energy change tells us the fraction of the initial energy that ends up in useful forms, and is usually expressed as a percentage:

$$\text{efficiency} = \frac{\text{useful output energy}}{\text{total input energy}} \times 100\%$$

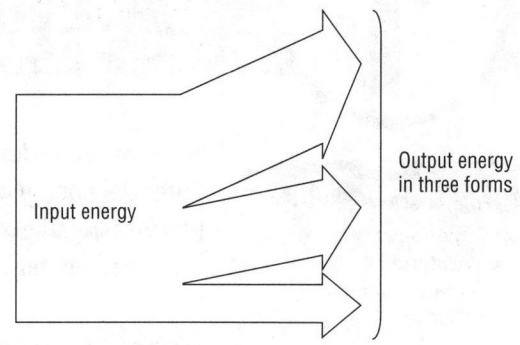

Note that efficiency is nearly always less than 100%, because heat energy is lost. (An electric heater could be considered to be 100% efficient.)

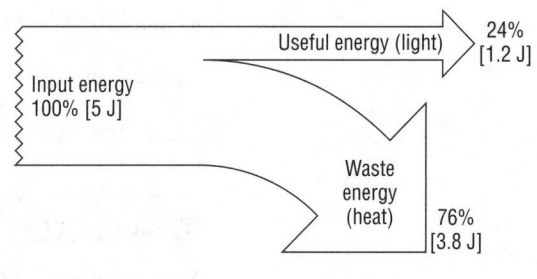

■ WORKED EXAMPLE

A **light-emitting diode** (LED) is supplied with 5.0 J of electrical energy each second, and produces 1.2 J of light energy and 3.8 J of heat energy. What is its efficiency?

STEP 1 Identify the useful output energy. In this case, it is light energy = 1.2 J

STEP 2 Calculate the efficiency.

$$\text{Efficiency} = \frac{1.2\text{ J}}{5.0\text{ J}} \times 100\% = 24\%$$

✔ *Quick check 5*

Module 3

Power

Power, *P*, is the rate of doing work, or the rate of transferring energy:

$$\text{power} = \frac{\text{work done}}{\text{time taken}} \qquad P = \frac{W}{t}$$

Power is measured in **watts, W**.

1 watt = 1 joule per second $1\text{ W} = 1\text{ J s}^{-1}$

1 kilowatt = 1 kW = 1000 J s⁻¹

✔ *Quick check 6, 7*

QUICK CHECK QUESTIONS ?

1   In the diagram at the top of the opposite page, gravity does 2500 J of work on the person as they fall. How much energy is transferred by this force?

2   A car's engine provides a forward force of 500 N. It is opposed by a resistive force of 200 N. The car accelerates forwards for 20 m. How much work is done by each force? By how much does the car's energy increase?

3   In the lower diagram on the opposite page, the person's weight *F* is 400 N and the distance they slide down the ramp is 8 m. If the angle of the slope to the horizontal is 30°, use the equation $W = Fx \cos\theta$ to calculate the work done by *F* in pulling them down the slope.

4   Show that $1\text{ J} = 1\text{ kg m}^2\text{ s}^{-2}$.

5   A light bulb is supplied with 60.0 J of electrical energy each second. It produces 58.5 J of heat energy in this time. What is the efficiency with which it produces light?

6   The engines of a light aircraft provide a power of 50 kW. How much energy do they transfer in 1 minute?

7   Calculate the power of an engine which transfers 30 kJ in 1 minute.

Hint

Take care! The angle between *F* and *x* is not 30°.

Kinetic and potential energy

Key words

- kinetic energy
- gravitational potential energy

Two important forms of energy are **kinetic energy** (KE) and **potential energy** (PE). Potential energy may be due to the position of an object in a gravitational field (**gravitational potential energy**, GPE), or due to its shape (elastic potential energy, explained on page 26).

Kinetic energy

A moving object has kinetic energy E_k, which depends on its mass m and its velocity v. Like all forms of energy, KE is measured in joules (J).

To calculate KE, we use:

$$E_k = \frac{1}{2}mv^2$$

Notice that this has the correct units of kg m^2 s^{-2}.

■ WORKED EXAMPLE

A car of mass 800 kg is moving at 15 m s^{-1}. What is its KE?

Substituting in $E_k = \frac{1}{2}mv^2$ gives:

$$E_k = \tfrac{1}{2} \times 800 \times 15^2 = \tfrac{1}{2} \times 800 \times 225 = 90\ 000\ \text{J}$$

✔ *Quick check 1, 2*

Gravitational potential energy

When an object of weight mg is raised through a height h, work is done against gravity. The energy given to the object as a result is called its **gravitational potential energy** (GPE). This is increased by an amount E_p given by:

gain in GPE = weight × gain in height; $E_p = mgh$

An object's GPE increases as it moves upwards (h is positive) and decreases as it moves downwards (h is negative).

✔ *Quick check 3, 4*

Note that the equation 'gain in GPE = weight × gain in height' is a form of the equation that defines *work done*, with force = weight and distance moved = gain in height.

KE and GPE changes

There are many situations where an object is moving up and down, and there is an interchange between KE and GPE. If no energy is lost as heat, we can assume that the change in KE is equal (and opposite) to the change in GPE. (This is an example of the principle of conservation of energy.)

We can write this as an equation,

$$E_k + E_p = \text{constant}$$

Hint

Air resistance results in the loss of energy as heat.

✓ *Quick check 5*

■ WORKED EXAMPLE

A stone falls from a height of 5 m. How fast is it moving when it reaches the ground?

STEP 1 The *decrease* in the stone's GPE as it falls is equal to its *gain* in KE.

$$mgh = \frac{1}{2}mv^2$$

STEP 2 Cancel m from both sides:

$$gh = \frac{1}{2}v^2$$

STEP 3 Substitute values and solve for v:

$$9.81 \text{ m s}^{-2} \times 5 \text{ m} = 0.5v^2$$
$$v^2 = 98.1 \text{ m}^2 \text{ s}^{-2}$$
$$v = 9.9 \text{ m s}^{-1}$$

Note that the fact that m cancels out means that we would get the same answer for any value of m, i.e. all stones of whatever mass would fall at the same rate (neglecting air resistance).

✓ *Quick check 6, 7*

Module 3

QUICK CHECK QUESTIONS

1 A stone of mass 2 kg is moving at 20 m s^{-1}. What is its KE?

2 A car of mass 600 kg accelerates from 10 m s^{-1} to 20 m s^{-1}. By how much has its KE increased?

3 A car of mass 1000 kg is travelling at 20 m s^{-1}. What is its kinetic energy? It climbs a hill 200 m high. By how much does its gravitational potential energy increase?

4 An aircraft of mass 400 000 kg is travelling at a height of 8000 m. It increases its height to 9500 m. By how much does its GPE increase? (In this example, use $g = 10$ m s^{-2}.)

5 As a stone falls, its GPE decreases by 20 J. By how much does its KE increase? What assumption is made in answering this question?

6 A rollercoaster car of mass 2000 kg runs downhill from a stationary start. If it runs downwards through a vertical height of 25 m, calculate its KE and speed at the foot of the hill. (Assume there are no frictional energy losses.)

7 A stone falls 5 m under gravity. Assuming that 2% of its energy is lost due to air resistance, with what speed is it moving at the lowest point of its fall?

Hint

Calculate the two values of KE, and subtract.

Deforming solids

Key words

- tensile
- compressive
- elastic limit
- force constant
- elastic potential energy
- stress
- strain
- Young modulus

It takes a pair of forces to *stretch* a solid object; such forces are called **tensile.** Forces which *squash* an object are called **compressive.** Tensile forces can stretch and break an object. It is easiest to start by describing how a spring stretches.

Hooke's law

The greater the **load** (the force stretching the spring), the greater its **extension** (increase in length). Eventually the load is so great that the spring becomes permanently stretched. The graph shows two things:

- At first the graph is a straight line, so load F is proportional to extension x; $F \propto x$.

- Beyond the **elastic limit**, the spring does not return to its original length when the load is removed.

Hint

You may find 'stiffness' easier to remember than 'force constant'.

The proportionality can be turned into an equation; the constant of proportionality is called the **force constant** k.

$$F = kx$$

k is measured in N m^{-1}. It is sometimes known as the *stiffness* of the spring. k tells you how many newtons are needed to stretch the spring by 1 metre.

✔ *Quick check 1*

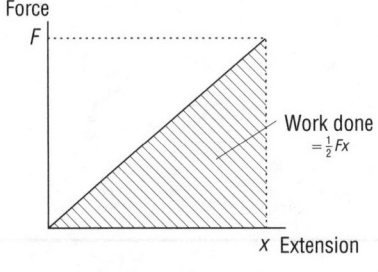

Elastic potential energy

An object that is stretched or compressed elastically is a store of **elastic potential energy**. The area under a force–extension graph is equal to the work done by the force. For a spring when the load is less than the elastic limit, the area under the graph is ½ × force × distance; this tells you the work done in stretching the spring, which is known as the elastic potential energy. This can be calculated as follows:

Elastic potential energy = ½ Fx = ½ kx^2

✔ *Quick check 2, 3*

Stretching a wire

Measure the original length of the test wire using a metre rule; measure its diameter using a micrometer, and calculate its cross-sectional area.

Gradually increase the load on the test wire. For each load, note the reading from the vernier scale.

Calculate values of stress and strain from values of load and extension, and plot a stress–strain graph.

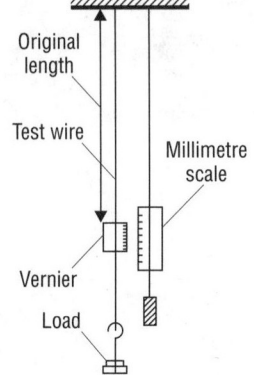

The extension x of the wire depends on four factors:

- its original length l,
- the load F stretching it,
- the cross-sectional area A,
- the stiffness of the material of which it is made.

These are combined as follows:

$$\text{strain} = \frac{\text{extension}}{\text{original length}} \qquad \text{strain} = \frac{x}{l}$$

$$\text{stress} = \frac{\text{load}}{\text{area}} \qquad \text{stress} = \frac{F}{A}$$

The greater the stress, the greater the strain that results. For many materials:

$$\frac{\text{stress}}{\text{strain}} = \text{constant}$$

and this constant is known as the **Young modulus**, Y, of the material. Y is measured in N m^{-2} or *pascals* (Pa). Its value is typically expressed in MPa or GPa (millions or billions of pascals); 1 MPa = 1 megapascal = 10^6 Pa; 1 GPa = 1 gigapascal = 10^9 Pa.

$$\text{Young modulus} = \frac{\text{stress}}{\text{strain}}$$

Stress–strain graphs

For low stresses, below the elastic limit (e.l.), the material will return to its original length when the load is removed. This is **elastic deformation**. For higher stresses, the material becomes permanently deformed. This is **plastic deformation.**

The Young modulus is the gradient of the *initial* (straight line) part of the graph. Once the stress reaches its highest value (the **ultimate tensile strength**, u.t.s.) the material will break.

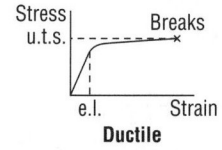
Ductile

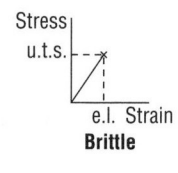
Brittle

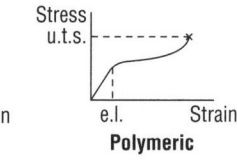
Polymeric

Materials may be classified as follows:

- A **ductile** material stretches a lot beyond the elastic limit, e.g. copper.
- A **brittle** material snaps when it reaches the elastic limit, e.g. glass.
- A **polymeric** material does not show linear behaviour, e.g. polythene.

Hint

You can think of stress as the same as pressure; each is a force divided by an area.

Examiner tip

You may be asked to describe how you would determine the Young modulus of a metal in the form of a wire.

✓ *Quick check 4*

✓ *Quick check 5*

Module 3

QUICK CHECK QUESTIONS

1 A spring is 1.2 m long when unstretched, and 1.4 m long when a load of 50 N is applied. Its elastic limit is 80 N. Calculate the extension produced by the 50 N load, and the spring's stiffness (force constant).

2 A spring is stretched elastically by a force of 400 N so that its length increases from 2.0 m to 2.4 m. Calculate the elastic potential energy stored.

3 A spring of force constant $k = 2400$ N m^{-1} is stretched by 5.0 cm. Calculate the elastic potential energy stored.

4 A stress of 20 MPa is applied to a wire of Young modulus 10 GPa. What strain is produced? If the wire's initial length was 0.8 m, what extension does the stress produce?

5 The table shows stress–strain data for an iron wire. Use the data to plot a stress–strain graph; deduce the Young modulus for iron; and state whether the wire shows plastic or brittle behaviour.

stress/MPa	0	50	100	150	200	250
strain (%)	0	0.025	0.050	0.075	0.100	wire breaks

End-of-unit questions

See Appendix 3 on page 79 for data and equations provided in the examination.

Module 1: Motion

1 a A quantity may be either a scalar or a vector quantity. Define *scalar* and *vector*.
   b Which of the following quantities are vectors, and which are scalars?
      Force, velocity, distance, acceleration, kinetic energy, power.

2 a Write down a word equation that defines acceleration.
   b The graph shows how the velocity of a car varied during the first part of a journey. Determine the car's acceleration during the parts of the journey represented by AB and BC.

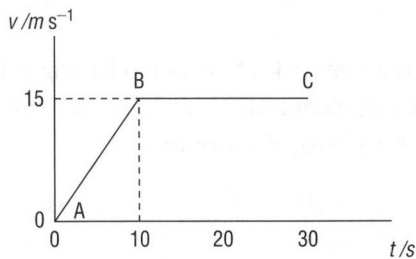

   c Copy the graph and add to it to indicate how you would expect the car's velocity to change if it was involved in a sudden collision with a brick wall.

3 The diagram shows a heavy load being dragged by two tractors. The tension in each cable is 20 kN.

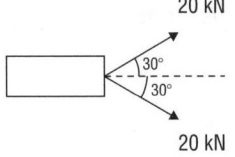

   Draw a vector triangle and use it to find the resultant of these two forces.

4 A car is travelling at 10 m s^{-1}. The driver accelerates at a rate of 2 m s^{-2} for 6 s.
   a How far does the car travel during this time?
   b What speed will it reach?

5 A boy stands on the edge of a cliff. He throws a stone upwards so that it leaves his hand, 2.0 m above the clifftop, with an initial velocity of 8.0 m s^{-1}. It rises upwards and then falls vertically downwards to the foot of the cliff.
   (You may assume that air resistance is negligible throughout the stone's motion.)
   a Calculate the greatest height to which the stone will rise (above the point where it leaves the boy's hand).
   b If the cliff is 20 m high, calculate the stone's vertical velocity when it reaches the foot of the cliff.
   c What is the stone's average velocity during its motion?
   d How much time elapses between the moment when the stone leaves the boy's hand and when it reaches the foot of the cliff?

6 Describe an experiment to measure the acceleration of free fall g, using a falling object. State the measurements you would make and how you would deduce the value of g from them.

Module 2: Forces in action

7 A box is being pulled along level ground. The diagram shows the horizontal forces acting on the box.

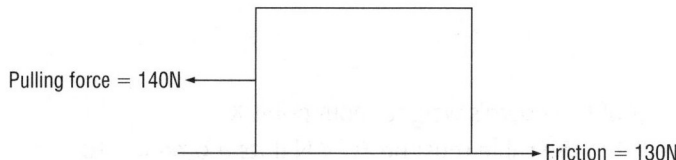

Pulling force = 140N

Friction = 130N

  a Calculate the resultant force acting on the box.
  b If the mass of the box is 40 kg, what is its acceleration?
  c If the volume of the box is 0.05 m³, what is its density?
  d The area of the box in contact with the ground is 0.12 m². What pressure does it exert on the ground?

8 a State the SI unit of force.
  b Write an equation to show how this unit is related to the kilogram, metre and second (three of the base units of the SI system).

9 When the space shuttle comes in to land, it deploys a parachute to slow it down. The graph shows how the horizontal force F on the shuttle varies with time t.

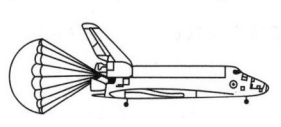 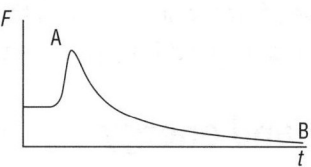

  a The parachute is deployed at point A on the graph. Explain why the force on the shuttle decreases in the region AB.
  b Copy the graph. On the same axes, add a further line to show how the shuttle's velocity changes.

10 a 'The gravitational field strength g at the Earth's surface is 9.81 N kg⁻¹.' Explain what is meant by this statement.
  b An astronaut measures his weight on Earth as 882 N. He travels to the surface of Mars, where the gravitational field strength is 3.8 N kg⁻¹. What will be the values of his mass and weight on Mars?
  c Show that 9.81 N kg⁻¹ is the same as 9.81 m s⁻².

Examiner tip

If you are asked to 'State …', give a concise answer without any supporting argument or description.

11 a With the aid of a diagram, explain what is meant by the moment of a force. The diagram shows a diving board that projects horizontally from point X. Its weight (2000 N) acts halfway along its length, as shown. It is supported by a cable attached 1 m from the far end, which makes an angle of 50° with the vertical.

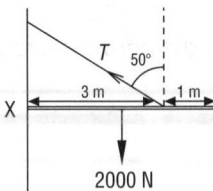

b Calculate the moment of the board's weight about point X.

c Show that the tension *T* in the cable must be 2074 N if its moment is to counteract the moment of the board's weight.

12 Police investigating a road accident discover that one of the cars has bald tyres; most of the tread has been worn away. They suggest to the driver that he should have noticed problems when he attempted to make the car accelerate.

a The driver claims that he was travelling at 20 m s⁻¹ when he braked. The police say that he should have been able to stop in a distance of 40 m if his tyres had been roadworthy. What would the driver's deceleration have been if he had stopped in this distance?

b Police tests show that the driver's bald tyres could not have provided a deceleration greater than 2 m s⁻². What braking distance would be required if the car was travelling at 20 m s⁻¹?

c The driver was saved from serious harm in the accident because his car was fitted with an air bag. Explain how this can reduce the impact force in a collision.

Hint

See Examiner tip on page 21.

Module 3: Work and energy

13 An aircraft of mass 100×10^3 kg is moving at 150 m s⁻¹. It reduces its height above the ground from 5000 m to 3000 m and increases its speed to 200 m s⁻¹. Calculate the change in its gravitational potential energy, and in its kinetic energy.

14 An experiment is conducted on a rubber cord of unstretched length 2.0 m. The cord has a rectangular cross-section of dimensions 0.5 mm by 5 mm. The cord is hung vertically and a weight of 100 N attached to its lower end. Its length increases to 2.4 m. Calculate:

a the stress in the cord

b the strain

c the Young modulus of the rubber.

15 A spring is stretched by hanging increasing weights on its end, and its length is measured for each value of the load. The table shows the results.

load (N)	0	10	20	30	40
length (m)	0.060	0.062	0.064	0.066	0.068

a Plot a suitable graph and use it to determine the force constant of the spring.

b The final load of 40 N does not exceed the spring's elastic limit. Explain what is meant by *elastic limit*.

c Use the graph to calculate the strain energy stored when the spring is stretched by the 40 N load.

16 a Sketch a force–extension graph for a ductile material.

b Indicate the regions in which you would expect its behaviour to be elastic, and where it will be plastic.

c State the essential difference between elastic and plastic deformation of a solid material.

Examiner tip

In an examination you may be expected to plot a graph on a grid printed in the exam booklet.
The axes may be labelled and units given, but if not, choose suitable scales and label the axes fully.

Examiner tip

If you are asked to sketch a graph, the shape and position of the curve need to be correct. Label the axes if they are not already labelled for you.

Electrons, waves and photons

There are five modules in this unit. It counts for 50% of the AS qualification.

The first three modules concern electric circuits. Then we look at waves and, finally, we consider some phenomena at the atomic scale where you have to learn to switch back and forth between wave and particle models to explain what is going on.

Module 1: Electric current considers electric current as a flow of charge.

Module 2: Resistance will help you to solve problems involving current, voltage and resistance, as well as energy and power in electric circuits.

Module 3: DC circuits looks at the difference between series and parallel circuits, and considers potential dividers as useful, practical circuits.

Module 4: Waves considers the basic properties of waves, including both mechanical and electromagnetic waves.

Module 5: Quantum physics looks at three phenomena (the photoelectric effect, electron diffraction and line spectra), and discusses when we need to consider light as particles rather than waves, and matter as waves rather than particles.

Your practical classes will have prepared you for the assessment of practical skills (Unit G483; see page v). There are some experiments that you must be able to describe as part of unit 2 (G482) for the examination. These are:

- an experiment to measure the I–V characteristics of a resistor at constant temperature, a filament lamp, and a light-emitting diode (page 39)
- experiments demonstrating two-source interference for sound, light and microwaves (pages 58 and 60)
- Young's double-slit experiment to demonstrate the wave nature of light (page 60)
- an experiment to determine the wavelength of monochromatic light using a laser and double slit (page 60)
- an experiment to determine the wavelength of light using a diffraction grating (page 61)
- experiments to demonstrate stationary waves using stretched strings, air columns and microwaves (pages 62–63)
- an experiment to determine the speed of sound using a pipe closed at one end (page 63).

For each experiment, you should be able to:

- sketch the appropriate apparatus and label it
- describe the measurements you would make
- show how to calculate the result
- comment on possible sources of error and inaccuracy.

Module 1 – Electric current, pages 34–35

Topic (in this book)	Reference to specification	Ideas from GCSE
Charge and current	2.1.1a–k	Measuring current

Module 2 – Resistance, pages 36–43

Topic (in this book)	Reference to specification	Ideas from GCSE
p.d. and e.m.f.	2.2.2a–f	Cells and batteries
Resistance	2.2.3a–g	Relationship between current, voltage and resistance
Resistivity	2.2.4a–d	
Electrical power	2.2.5a–g	Energy and power

Module 3 – DC circuits, pages 44–47

Topic (in this book)	Reference to specification	Ideas from GCSE
e.m.f. and internal resistance	2.3.1a, b, f, g, h	
Practical circuits	2.3.1c, d, e 2.3.2a–f	Resistors in series and parallel

Module 4 – Waves, pages 48–63

Topic (in this book)	Reference to specification	Ideas from GCSE
Wave representations	2.4.1a, e	Longitudinal and transverse waves
Wave quantities	2.4.1b	Frequency, wavelength, amplitude and speed of a wave
Wave speed	2.4.1b, c, d	Waves transferring energy
The electromagnetic spectrum	2.4.2a–e	Electromagnetic radiation
Polarisation	2.4.2f–h 2.4.3g	
Interference and diffraction	2.4.3a–f	Reflection and refraction of waves
Interference of light	2.4.3h–m	
Superposition and stationary waves	2.4.4a–h	

Module 5 – Quantum physics, pages 64–70

Topic (in this book)	Reference to specification	Ideas from GCSE
Photons	2.5.1a, b, c, d	
The photoelectric effect	2.5.2a–f	
Wave–particle duality	2.5.1e, f 2.5.3a–d	
Spectra	2.5.4a–c	Flame tests

End-of-unit questions, pages 72–74

UNIT 2

Charge and current

A battery pushes charge around a circuit. A current is a flow of charge. In metals, the charge is carried by **electrons**, which are negatively charged. However, before electrons were discovered, it was assumed that positive charge flows from the positive to the negative terminal, and we still use this convention today. The **conventional current** is from positive to negative, but in fact electrons flow around the circuit from the negative to the positive terminal.

In an electrolyte (a conducting solution), the mobile charges are positive and negative ions, moving in opposite directions.

Conservation of current

Current is the rate of flow of charge. Charge cannot disappear or get used up. For this reason, we say that **current is conserved**.

- At point X, current splits up:
  $$I = I_1 + I_2$$
- At point Y, currents recombine:
  $$I_1 + I_2 = I$$

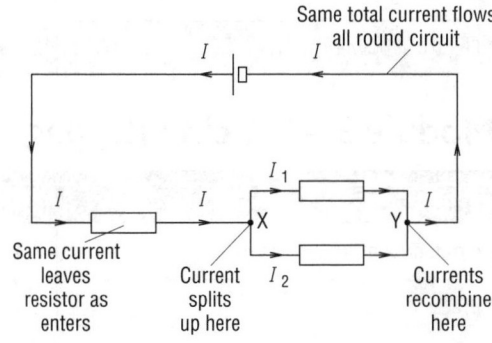

These equations describe the conservation of current. They are an example of **Kirchhoff's first law**. A more formal statement is:

The sum of the currents entering a point in a circuit is equal to the sum of the currents leaving the point.

$$\Sigma I_{in} = \Sigma I_{out}$$ where Σ (sigma) means 'the sum of'.

To measure current, an ammeter is connected in series in a circuit.

Coulombs and amps

Charge Q is measured in **coulombs** (C).
Current I is measured in amperes, **amps** (A).
One amp is one coulomb per second: $1\,A = 1\,C\,s^{-1}$.
One coulomb is the charge that passes when a current of 1 amp flows for 1 second.

Formulae relating Q, I and t

To calculate the current I flowing when charge ΔQ passes a point in time interval Δt:

$$I = \frac{\Delta Q}{\Delta t}$$

To calculate the charge:

$$\Delta Q = I \times \Delta t$$

The bigger the current, and the longer it flows, the more the charge that passes.

✓ *Quick check 1, 2*

Hint

The ampere is a base unit in the SI system; other electrical units are defined in terms of the ampere.

✓ *Quick check 3*

Hint

Dividing by time reminds us that current is a *rate* of flow.

■ WORKED EXAMPLE 1

What is the current when a charge of 600 C passes a point in 1 minute?

STEP 1 Write down what you know, and what you want to know:
$$\Delta Q = 600 \text{ C}, \Delta t = 60 \text{ s}, I = ?$$
STEP 2 Choose the appropriate equation, substitute and solve:

$$I = \frac{\Delta Q}{\Delta t} = \frac{600 \text{ C}}{60 \text{ s}} = 10 \text{ A}$$

Hint

Use SI units.

Don't forget units. Strictly speaking, this is the average current flowing in this time.

■ WORKED EXAMPLE 2

How much charge passes a point when a current of 10 mA is supplied for 10 s?

STEP 1 Write down what you know, and what you want to know:
$$I = 10 \text{ mA (or } 10^{-2} \text{ A or } 0.01 \text{ A)}, \Delta t = 10 \text{ s}, \Delta Q = ?$$
STEP 2 Choose the appropriate equation, substitute and solve:
$$\Delta Q = I \times \Delta t$$
$$= 10 \text{ mA} \times 10 \text{ s} = 100 \text{ mC}$$

Hint

Since we are working in mA (milliamps), the answer is in mC (millicoulombs). We could have converted from mA to A.

✓*Quick check 4, 5*

Drift velocity

The conduction electrons in a metal move around rapidly, in random directions. When a voltage is applied, the electrons gain an additional velocity along the wire. The **mean drift velocity** v is the average extra velocity gained by the electrons. The greater the current I, the greater the value of v.

The current also depends on the cross-sectional area A of the conductor, and on the **number density** n of electrons in the metal.

$$I = Anev$$

Metals have high number densities of electrons, so drift velocities are low – of the order of mm s⁻¹. Semiconductors have far fewer free electrons (n is much smaller), so drift velocities are much higher. For insulators, n is close to zero.

Hint

e is the electron charge.
n is the number of electrons per m³. n has the unit m⁻³.

✓*Quick check 6, 7*

QUICK CHECK QUESTIONS

1 Calculate current I_4, as shown in the figure.

2 Currents of 2.5 A, 1.0 A and 10.5 A are supplied by a car battery. What is the total current it supplies?

3 Define the coulomb.

4 What is the current if 240 mC of charge flows past a point in 30 s?

5 A motorist is having trouble getting his car to start. The battery supplies a current of 100 A for 1 minute. How much charge flows from the battery in this time?

6 Calculate the current in a copper wire of cross-sectional area 1 mm² if the mean drift velocity of the electrons is 2 mm s⁻¹. (Number density for copper = 10^{29} m⁻³; electron charge $e = 1.6 \times 10^{-19}$ C)

7 What is the mean drift velocity of electrons in a piece of semiconductor of cross-sectional area 2 mm² and number density 10^{23} m⁻³ when a current of 0.1 mA is supplied?

$I_4 = ?$
$I_1 = 2 \text{ A}$ $I_3 = 1 \text{ A}$
$I_2 = 4 \text{ A}$

p.d. and e.m.f.

Key words

- potential difference
- electromotive force

We use electricity to transfer energy from place to place. If you use a battery to light a bulb, electricity transfers energy from the battery to the bulb. The *voltage* of a source of electricity is a measure of these energy transfers.

We use two (more correct) terms for voltage:

- potential difference, p.d., symbol *V*
- electromotive force, e.m.f., symbol *E*

Around a circuit

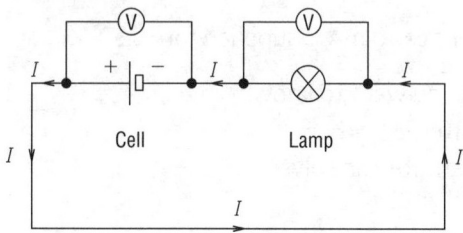

In this circuit, the cell is pushing a current (a flow of charge) through the lamp.

The current is the same at all points around the circuit.

- ***Inside the cell:*** charge flows through the cell, collecting energy.
- ***Inside the lamp:*** the same charge flows through the lamp, giving up energy.

The voltmeters give equal but opposite readings (positive and negative).

The meaning of e.m.f. and p.d.

The voltage shown on a cell or battery tells you its **e.m.f.** From this, you can tell the amount of energy given to each coulomb of charge passing around the circuit, including *through the cell itself.* In practice the useful p.d. across an appliance is less than the e.m.f. because some voltage is 'lost' pushing current through the cell.

- A 1.5 V cell gives 1.5 J to each coulomb.
- A 6 V battery gives 6 J to each coulomb.
- The 230 V mains gives 230 J to each coulomb.

Remember: The e.m.f. of a supply is the work it does in pushing 1 C of charge around a complete circuit.

Similarly, the **p.d.** across a component is the energy transferred by each coulomb of charge passing through it.

Examiner tip

Take care always to talk about the potential difference *across* a component, or *between* two points. A p.d. does not 'go through' a component.

Hint

Note that the current inside the cell flows from negative to positive – see page 44.

Formulae and units

Both p.d. V and e.m.f. E are measured in volts (V).

Energy W is measured in joules (J).

Charge Q is measured in coulombs (C).

Energy transferred = voltage × charge: $W = VQ$

One volt is one joule per coulomb: $1\,V = 1\,J\,C^{-1}$.

Combining e.m.f.s

When two or more cells (or other sources of e.m.f.) are connected in series, their voltages add up. Take care! They must be connected positive-to-negative; otherwise the e.m.f.s subtract, as in the third example.

$E = 1.5\,V$ $\qquad E = 4 \times 1.5\,V = 6\,V$ $\qquad E = 3 \times 1.5\,V - 1.5\,V = 3\,V$

Using a voltmeter

A voltmeter must be connected *across* the terminals of a component to measure the p.d. across it; in other words, it must be connected *in parallel* with it. You can remember this by recalling that the voltmeter is measuring the p.d. *across* the component.

(An ammeter is connected in series because the current it is measuring must flow *through* it.)

✓ *Quick check 1, 2*

Hint

Think of W for work. Avoid using E for energy.

✓ *Quick check 3–5*

Hint

There is no need to consider cells connected in parallel.

✓ *Quick check 6–8*

Module 2

QUICK CHECK QUESTIONS

1   How much energy is transferred to each coulomb of charge by a 9 V battery?

2   Which types of voltage are described here?
    a   a measure of the energy transferred to electric charges by a supply
    b   a measure of the energy transferred from electric charges to a component in a circuit.

3   10 C of charge flows through a p.d. of 6.0 V. How much energy is transferred?

4   How much work is done by the 230 V mains supply in pushing 1 C of charge round a circuit?

5   A current of 2.5 A flows through a resistor for 1 minute. It transfers 600 J of energy to the resistor. What is the p.d. across the resistor?

6   How many 1.2 V rechargeable batteries must be connected in series to provide an e.m.f. of 6.0 V?

7   A car battery consists of six 2.0 V cells connected in series. Draw a diagram to represent this and calculate the e.m.f. of the battery.

8   a   What is the e.m.f. provided by the combination of cells shown in the diagram?
    b   What e.m.f. would they provide if the connections to the 2.5 V cell were reversed?

       2.0 V   1.5 V 2.5 V   3.0 V

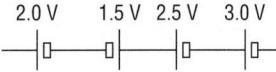

Hint

Start by calculating how much charge flows.

Resistance

Key words

• resistance
• ohmic conductor

A **potential difference** (p.d.) is needed to push a current through a component. The **electrical resistance** of the component tells us how difficult it is to make charge flow through it.

Defining resistance

The **resistance** R of a component is the ratio of the p.d. V across it to the current I flowing through it. It is defined by the equation:

$$\text{resistance} = \frac{\text{p.d.}}{\text{current}} \qquad R = \frac{V}{I}$$

The equation for resistance can be rearranged in two ways:

$$V = IR \qquad I = \frac{V}{R}$$

Hint

The greater the resistance, the smaller the current that flows for a given p.d.

Ohms, amps and volts

Resistance is measured in **ohms** (Ω).

One ohm is one volt per amp: $1\,\Omega = 1\,\text{V A}^{-1}$.

So it takes a p.d. of 1 V to make a current of 1 A flow through a 1 Ω resistor, and it takes a p.d. of 10 V to make a current of 1 A flow through a 10 Ω resistor.

• 1 kilo-ohm = 1 kΩ = $10^3\,\Omega$ = 1000 Ω
• 1 mega-ohm = 1 MΩ = $10^6\,\Omega$ = 1 000 000 Ω

Hint

The symbol Ω is the Greek letter omega.

✓ *Quick check 1, 2*

Ohm's law

A potential difference (p.d.), or **voltage**, pushes current through a conductor. The greater the p.d., the greater the current. An **ohmic conductor** is one in which the current that flows is proportional to the p.d. that pushes it. It obeys **Ohm's law**.

Remembering the equation $V = IR$, this means that the resistance of the conductor is constant, and does not depend on the p.d. across it.

Measuring resistance

• An **ammeter** connected *in series* measures the current through the resistor.

• A **voltmeter** connected *in parallel* measures the p.d. across the resistor.

• Reversing the connections to the resistor makes the current flow through it in the opposite direction. This gives negative values of current I and voltage V.

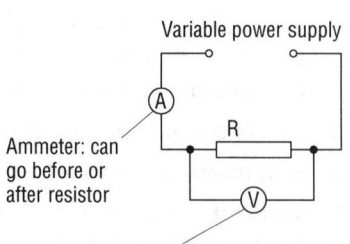

Variable power supply

Ammeter: can go before or after resistor

Voltmeter: usually connected last

Current–voltage graphs

The results can be plotted as a **current–voltage characteristic** graph, or *I–V* graph. The lower figure on the right shows an *I–V* graph for a metallic conductor at constant temperature. An ohmic conductor gives a straight line through the origin.

It is usual to plot p.d. on the *x*-axis.

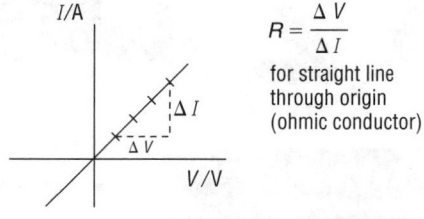

$$R = \frac{\Delta V}{\Delta I}$$

for straight line through origin (ohmic conductor)

✔*Quick check 3*

Non-ohmic conductors

Metals obey Ohm's law – they are ohmic conductors – provided the temperature remains constant. A **non-ohmic conductor** has an *I–V* characteristic graph that is not a straight line. The figure below shows *I–V* graphs for an ohmic conductor and a non-ohmic conductor (a filament lamp).

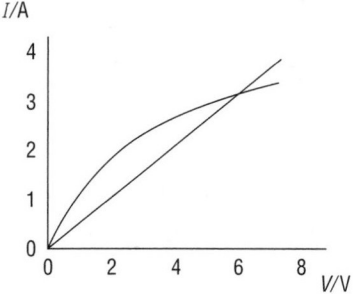

✔*Quick check 4*

Filament lamp: As the metal filament gets hotter with increasing current and voltage, its resistance increases. The current is less than it would be if it remained proportional to the voltage.

Semiconductor diode: In the forward direction, this allows current to flow when the p.d. is above 0.7 V. In the reverse direction, only a very small current flows. A light-emitting diode (LED) shows a similar pattern; it emits light when a sufficiently large current flows through it.

Advantages of LEDs as light sources
They:
- require only low p.d.
- have a long working life
- are very robust
- can be used singly as indicators or in large arrays to illuminate
- switch on instantly.

QUICK CHECK QUESTIONS

1   What is the resistance of a resistor if a p.d. of 10 V makes a current of 2 A pass through it?

2   What p.d. will make a current of 20 mA pass through a 500 kΩ resistor?

3   The table shows experimental results for a carbon resistor of resistance *R*. Plot a graph and use it to deduce *R*.

current *I* (mA)	180	340	550	700	910
p.d. *V* (V)	2.0	4.0	6.0	8.0	10.0

4   Use the graph in the figure above to decide at what voltage the filament lamp and the resistor have the same resistance *R*. What is the value of *R*?

Hint

Recall that an ohm is a volt per amp.

Module 2

Resistivity

Key words

- resistivity
- thermistor

✓ Quick check 1, 2

The resistance of a wire depends on two geometrical factors:

- its length l – the longer the wire, the greater its resistance: $R \propto l$
- its cross-sectional area A – the fatter the wire, the less its resistance: $R \propto 1/A$.

So, doubling the length of a wire doubles its resistance; doubling its cross-sectional area *halves* its resistance.

A material property

Some materials resist the flow of electric current more than others. The property that describes this is **resistivity**, ρ (Greek letter rho).

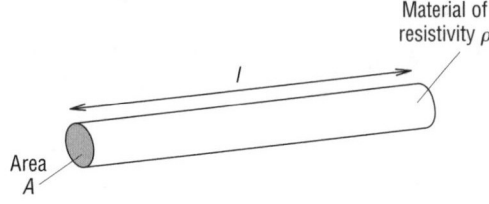
Material of resistivity ρ

Area A

To determine the resistance R of a wire, for example, we need to know the resistivity of the material it is made of: $R \propto \rho$ (ρ is a constant for a given material, at a given temperature). The formula is:

$$R = \frac{\rho l}{A} \text{ or } \rho = \frac{RA}{l}$$

The second of these equations defines resistivity.

Resistivity is measured in Ω **m (ohm metres)**.

A typical value for a good conductor: resistivity of copper = $1.6 \times 10^{-8}\ \Omega$ m.

Hint

Take care – not ohms per metre!

■ WORKED EXAMPLE 1

A wire of length 120 m and cross-sectional area 0.1 mm² is made from an alloy of gold and silver. Its resistance is measured and found to be 19.2 Ω. What is the resistivity of the alloy?

STEP 1 Write down what you know, and what you want to know.
$l = 120$ m, $R = 19.2\ \Omega$, $A = 1 \times 10^{-7}$ m², $\rho = ?$

STEP 2 Calculate ρ.
$\rho = RA/l = 19.2\ \Omega \times 1 \times 10^{-7}$ m² $/ 120$ m $= 1.6 \times 10^{-8}\ \Omega$ m

---

■ WORKED EXAMPLE 2

What is the resistance of a 20 m length of silver wire of diameter 1 mm? (Resistivity of silver = $1.6 \times 10^{-8}\ \Omega$ m.)

STEP 1 Write down what you know, and what you want to know; you will have to calculate A.
$l = 20$ m, $\rho = 1.6 \times 10^{-8}\ \Omega$ m, $A = \pi r^2 = \pi \times (0.5 \times 10^{-3}$ m$)^2 = 7.85 \times 10^{-7}$ m², $R = ?$

STEP 2 Calculate R.

$$R = \frac{\rho l}{A} = \frac{1.6 \times 10^{-8}\ \Omega \text{ m} \times 20 \text{ m}}{7.85 \times 10^{-7} \text{ m}^2} = 0.41\ \Omega$$

Hint

Remember to halve the diameter to find the radius.

✓ Quick check 3–5

Temperature dependence

There are several factors that can affect the resistivity of a material. An important factor is temperature.

When a metal is heated, its resistivity increases. This is because, as the temperature rises, the atoms of the metal vibrate with increasing amplitude. This makes it more likely that conduction electrons will collide with the atoms as they try to travel through the metal. The electrons lose energy when they collide, and so we observe an increase in the metal's resistivity.

A semiconductor has many fewer conduction electrons than a metal (its number density is less – see page 35). When a semiconductor is heated, more electrons break free from their atoms, increasing the number of free electrons that can carry the current (the number density increases rapidly). So the resistivity of the semiconductor decreases as it is heated – the opposite of a metal.

The figure shows two examples.

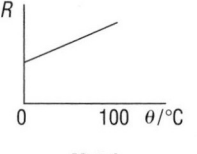
Metal

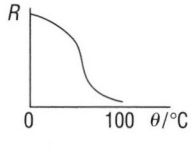
NTC thermistor

✓*Quick check 6*

- **Metal:** resistance increases gradually as temperature is increased.
- **NTC thermistor:** resistance decreases rapidly over a narrow range of temperature.

NTC means 'negative temperature coefficient': resistance goes down as temperature goes up.

QUICK CHECK QUESTIONS

1. Wires A and B are made of the same material. Wire A has twice the length of wire B; wire B has half the cross-sectional area of wire A. Which wire has the greater resistance, A or B, or are they both the same?

2. A 5 m length of wire is found to have a resistance of 240 Ω. What will be the resistance of a 50 cm piece of the wire?

3. What is the resistance of a 5 m length of copper wire of cross-sectional area 1 mm²? (Resistivity of copper = 1.6×10^{-8} Ω m.)

4. A 1 m length of tin wire, diameter 1.2 mm, is found to have a resistance of 0.097 Ω. Calculate the resistivity of tin.

5. What will be the resistance per metre length of a nickel wire of diameter 0.8 mm? (Resistivity of nickel = 5.9×10^{-7} Ω m.)

6. Does the resistivity of a metal increase or decrease with temperature? And of a semiconductor?

> **Hint**
>
> 1 mm² = 10^{-6} m².

UNIT 2

Electrical power

Module 2

We use electricity as a convenient way of transferring energy from place to place. *Voltage* is a measure of how much energy is transferred to or from each coulomb of charge. *Current* tells us about the rate at which charge moves. Combining these quantities tells us about the *rate* at which energy is transferred by a current – the **electrical power**.

Power in general

We met the general idea of *power* on page 23. Power is the rate at which energy is transferred.

$$\text{power} = \frac{\text{energy transferred}}{\text{time taken}} \qquad P = \frac{W}{t}$$

$$\text{energy transferred} = \text{power} \times \text{time} \qquad W = Pt$$

Units

Power is measured in **watts**, W.

1 watt = 1 joule per second; $1\,\text{W} = 1\,\text{J s}^{-1}$

1 kilowatt = $1\,\text{kW} = 10^3\,\text{W} = 1000\,\text{W}$

1 megawatt = $1\,\text{MW} = 10^6\,\text{W} = 1\,000\,000\,\text{W}$

1 gigawatt = $1\,\text{GW} = 10^9\,\text{W} = 1\,000\,000\,000\,\text{W}$

Calculating electrical power

The greater the current I and the greater the p.d. V that it is flowing through, the greater the power P.

$$\text{power} = \text{current} \times \text{p.d.}; \qquad P = IV$$

Combining this equation with $V = IR$ gives two alternative forms:

$$P = I^2R \text{ and } P = \frac{V^2}{R}$$

The equation for energy transferred W becomes:

$$\text{energy transferred} = \text{current} \times \text{p.d.} \times \text{time} \qquad W = IVt$$

■ **WORKED EXAMPLE**

A car headlamp bulb is labelled '12 V, 48 W'. What is its resistance in normal operation? (The label indicates its normal operating voltage and power.)

STEP 1 Write down what you know, and what you want to know:
$$V = 12\,V, P = 48\,W, R = ?$$
STEP 2 Select the appropriate equation and rearrange it to make R the subject:
$$P = \frac{V^2}{R} \text{ so } R = \frac{V^2}{P}$$
STEP 3 Substitute values and calculate the answer:
$$R = \frac{(12\,V)^2}{48\,W} = 3\,\Omega$$

Key words

- power
- kilowatt-hour

Hint

Mechanical power is the rate at which energy is transferred by a force – see page 23.

✔ *Quick check 1, 2*

Hint

You may find it easier to remember this as watts = amps × volts.

Examiner tip

Choose the form of equation according to the information you have in any question.

✔ *Quick check 3*

✔ *Quick check 4, 5*

Another energy unit – the kilowatt-hour (kWh)

Electricity is usually charged for in units of kilowatt-hours.

A 1 kW heater used for 1 h transfers 1 kWh of energy.

A 2 kW heater used for 5 h transfers 10 kWh of energy.

> **Energy transferred (kWh) = power (kW) × time (h)**

1 kWh = 3 600 000 J = 3.6 MJ, because 1 kW = 1000 J s^{-1} and 1 h = 3600 s.

> **Hint**
>
> A joule is a small amount of energy. It's often easier to work in kilowatt-hours.

✓ *Quick check 6, 7*

SI units summary

It is often easier to learn equations linking units rather than quantities.

Quantity	Unit	Equivalents	In words
current I	ampere, A	1 A = 1 C s^{-1}	amp = coulomb per second
p.d. V, e.m.f. E	volt, V	1 V = 1 J C^{-1}	volt = joule per coulomb
resistance R	ohm, Ω	1 Ω = 1 V A^{-1}	ohm = volt per amp
power P	watt, W	1 W = 1 J s^{-1}	watt = joule per second

Fuses

Electrical appliances are protected from dangerous overloading by the fuse in the plug. The fuse is made of thin copper wire in a ceramic casing. Above a certain value of current, the wire becomes so hot that it melts, breaking the circuit. A fuse should be chosen so that its rating is a little higher than the maximum current drawn by the device when it is operating correctly. You can calculate this from its voltage and power rating using $P = IV$. Most household appliances use fuses of 3 A, 5 A or 13 A.

■ WORKED EXAMPLE

What fuse should you use in the plug of a 1 kW electric fire connected to the household mains (230 V)?

STEP 1 Write down what you know and what you want to know:
   $P = 1 \text{ kW} = 1000 \text{ W}, V = 230 \text{ V}, I = ?$

STEP 2 Select and rearrange the equation you need:
   $P = IV$ so $I = P/V$

STEP 3 Calculate the answer:
   $I = (1000 \text{ W})/(230 \text{ V}) = 4.3 \text{ A}$ so a 5 A fuse is needed.

QUICK CHECK QUESTIONS

1 The output of a power station is stated as 450 MW. How many joules of electrical energy does it supply each second?

2 A battery transfers 30 J of energy each minute. What power is this?

3 A 1.5 V cell passes a current of 0.4 A through a lamp for 5 minutes. How much energy is transferred to the lamp?

4 An electric motor draws a current of 2.5 A from a 12 V supply. What power does it transfer?

5 A 60 W lamp has a resistance of 2.4 Ω. What current flows through it in normal operation?

6 A 150 W light bulb is left on for 24 hours. How many kW h of energy are transferred in this time?

7 A 2.5 kWh heater is switched on for an average of 8 h each day. If each kWh of electricity costs 7 p, what is the average daily cost of using the heater?

e.m.f. and internal resistance

Key words

- internal resistance
- lost volts

We use a cell or power supply to provide a p.d. Sometimes it provides less than we expect, because of its **internal resistance**.

Internal resistance

Think about the current flowing around a circuit, pushed by a cell or power supply. The same current flows all the way round. In particular, it flows through the *interior* of the supply (from negative to positive). The interior of a supply is made up of chemicals or metal wire, and must have resistance. This is the internal resistance *r* of the supply.

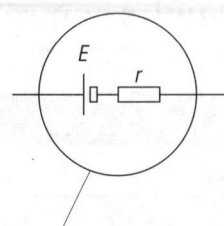

The circle is optional; it indicates that *E* and *r* are part of the same thing

We show the cell as a 'perfect cell', marked with its e.m.f. *E*, and a small resistor *r* in series with it. The current *I* flows through a combined resistance $R + r$.

$$E = I(R + r)$$

$$E = V + Ir$$

The circle is optional; it indicates that *E* and *r* are part of the same thing.

e.m.f. = terminal p.d. of cell + lost volts

We get fewer volts across the terminals of the supply because some of the e.m.f. is used up (or lost) in overcoming the internal resistance when a current is flowing.

Measuring *E* and *r*

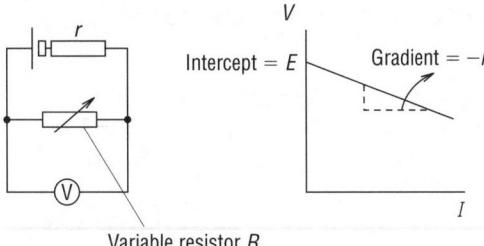

Variable resistor *R*

Intercept = *E*   Gradient = −*r*

Varying the value of *R* makes the current *I* change. The graph shows that the greater the current that flows from the supply, the smaller its terminal p.d. The graph is roughly a straight line:

- gradient = −*r*,
- intercept on *y*-axis = *E*.

Using a high-resistance voltmeter

A digital voltmeter has a resistance of millions of ohms. Connect it across a supply, and only a tiny (negligible) current will flow. Its reading will therefore indicate the e.m.f. of the supply ('lost volts' = 0).

Hint

The meaning of e.m.f. was explained on page 36.

Hint

The e.m.f. of a supply is the p.d. across its terminals when no current flows.

Quick check 1, 2

■ WORKED EXAMPLE

A power supply of e.m.f. 6 V and internal resistance 2 Ω is connected across a 10 Ω resistor. What current flows through the resistor, and what is the terminal p.d. of the supply?

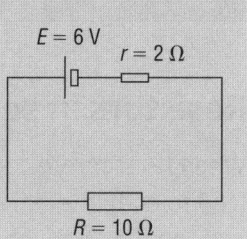

STEP 1 Draw a diagram, showing both R and r.
STEP 2 Calculate the total resistance in the circuit.
$$R + r = 10\ \Omega + 2\ \Omega = 12\ \Omega$$
STEP 3 Calculate the current that flows.
$$I = \frac{E}{R + r} = \frac{6\ \text{V}}{12\ \Omega} = 0.5\ \text{A}$$
STEP 4 Calculate the terminal p.d.
$$V = IR = 0.5\ \text{A} \times 10\ \Omega = 5\ \text{V}$$

> **Hint**
>
> 1 V has been 'lost' in overcoming the internal resistance.

✔ *Quick check 3*

Kirchhoff's second law

Trace the movement of 1 C of charge around the circuit:

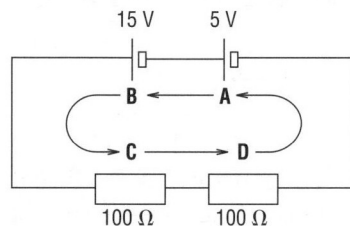

- at **A**: 5 J gained
- at **B**: 15 J gained; total energy gained = 20 J
- at **C**: 10 J lost
- at **D**: 10 J lost; total energy lost = 20 J.

By the time the charge has completed the circuit, it has lost as much energy as it gained. This is an example of **conservation of energy**. We can think of this in terms of voltages around the circuit:

Kirchhoff's second law:

The sum of the e.m.f.s around any circuit loop is equal to the sum of the p.d.s: $\Sigma E = \Sigma IR$.

✔ *Quick check 4, 5*

QUICK CHECK QUESTIONS

1 A power supply of e.m.f. 500 V and internal resistance 0.10 Ω is connected to a heater of resistance 125 Ω. What current flows through the heater?

2 A high-resistance voltmeter is connected across a cell so that no current flows; it gives a reading of 1.55 V. A 600 Ω resistor is added in parallel with the voltmeter, which now reads 1.50 V. What are the e.m.f. and internal resistance of the cell?

3 A 5 V supply of internal resistance 5 Ω is connected across a 20 Ω resistor. What is the terminal p.d. of the supply?

4 Two resistors are connected in series with the 230 V mains supply. The p.d. across one resistor is 70 V. What is the p.d. across the other?

5 Calculate:
 a the total e.m.f. in this circuit;
 b the current around it;
 c the p.d. across each resistor.
 d Show that Kirchhoff's second law is satisfied.

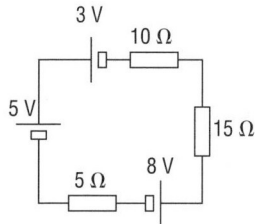

> **Hint**
>
> Give your answer to three decimal places.

Module 3

Practical circuits

Key words

- in series
- in parallel
- potential divider

Resistors in series

When resistors are connected **in series** (end to end), the current flows through one and then through the next, and so on.

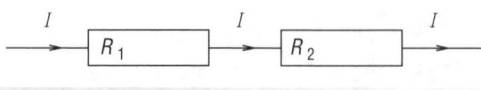

- Resistors in series must have the *same current* through them.

- The p.d. of the supply is *shared* between them.

To find the combined resistance R of two or more resistors in series, add up their individual resistances:

$R = R_1 + R_2 + R_3 + \ldots$ **in series**

■ WORKED EXAMPLE

A 20 Ω resistor and a 5 Ω resistor are connected in series with a 10 V battery. What is the p.d. across each resistor?

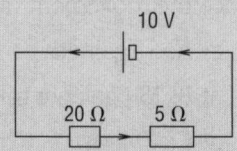

STEP 1 Sketch a diagram; calculate the combined resistance:

$R = R_1 + R_2 = 20\ \Omega + 5\ \Omega = 25\ \Omega$

STEP 2 Calculate the current that flows:

$I = \dfrac{V}{R} = \dfrac{10\ V}{25\ \Omega} = 0.4\ A$

STEP 3 Calculate the p.d. across each resistor:

Across 20 Ω: $V = IR = 0.4\ A \times 20\ \Omega = 8\ V$

Across 5 Ω: $V = IR = 0.4\ A \times 5\ \Omega = 2\ V$

Hint

A useful rule: the bigger resistor gets a bigger share of the p.d.

✓*Quick check 1*

Resistors in parallel

When resistors are connected **in parallel** (side-by-side), the current divides up, part of it flowing through each resistor.

- Resistors in parallel have the *same p.d.* across them.

- The current flowing from the supply is *shared* between them.

Since $I = V/R$ for *each* resistor, to find the combined resistance R of two or more resistors in parallel, add up the *reciprocals* of their individual resistances:

$\dfrac{1}{R} = \dfrac{1}{R_1} + \dfrac{1}{R_2} + \dfrac{1}{R_3} + \ldots$ **in parallel**

■ WORKED EXAMPLE

A 20 Ω resistor and a 5 Ω resistor are connected in parallel with a 10 V battery. What current flows from the battery?

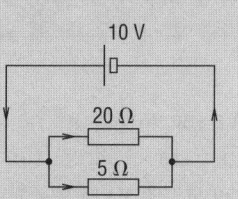

STEP 1 Sketch a diagram; calculate (in two stages!) the combined resistance:

$$\frac{1}{R} = \frac{1}{R_1} + \frac{1}{R_2} = \frac{1}{20\,\Omega} + \frac{1}{5\,\Omega} = 0.05\,\Omega^{-1} + 0.20\,\Omega^{-1} = 0.25\,\Omega^{-1}$$

$$R = \frac{1}{0.25\,\Omega^{-1}} = 4\,\Omega$$

(For resistances connected in parallel, R is always *less than* the smallest of R_1, R_2, etc.)

STEP 2 Calculate the current from the combined resistance and the p.d.:

$$I = \frac{V}{R} = \frac{10\,V}{4\,\Omega} = 2.5\,A$$

Hint

Another method: calculate the current through each resistor separately, and add them together.

✔ *Quick check 2, 3*

Potential dividers

You can reduce the p.d. provided by a supply by connecting two resistors across its terminals. Tap off the required p.d. (V_{out}) from the point between them.

The bigger resistor takes the bigger share of the p.d.

Use equal resistors to give half the p.d. of the supply.

To find V_{out} use the equation $V_{out} = \dfrac{R_2}{R_1 + R_2} \times V_{in}$

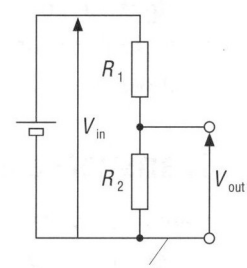

Consider the bottom line as 0 V

Varying resistances

- Shining light on the LDR (light-dependent resistor) will decrease its resistance. V_{out} will decrease.

- Warming the NTC thermistor will decrease its resistance. V_{out} will decrease.

Swap the resistors over if you want V_{out} to increase.

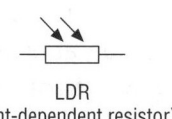

LDR
(light-dependent resistor)

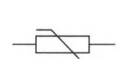

NTC thermistor

✔ *Quick check 4, 5*

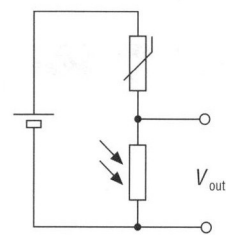

QUICK CHECK QUESTIONS

1 Two 20 Ω resistors are connected in series with a 5 V supply. What is the p.d. across each resistor?

2 What is the resistance of 20 Ω, 30 Ω, 60 Ω resistors connected in parallel?

3 Three 2 kΩ resistors are connected in parallel across a 12 V supply. What current flows from the supply?

4 Calculate V_{out} as shown in the figure. Notice that one resistor has twice the resistance of the other.

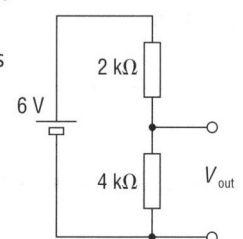

Examiner tip

Using the potential divider equation is quicker than calculating the current and then the voltages.

5 A potential divider is constructed from a 50 Ω fixed resistor and a thermistor whose resistance changes from 450 Ω at 20 °C to 50 Ω at 80 °C. The divider is connected across a 10 V supply. Draw a diagram of this arrangement, and show that its output voltage will vary between 9 V and 5 V as the temperature is varied between 20 °C and 80 °C.

Module 3

Wave representations

Key words

- sine wave
- electromagnetic wave
- reflection
- refraction
- diffraction

Hint

Although we may represent a sound wave using a sine curve, the particles move back and forth, not up and down.

We see waves on the surface of water. They travel across the surface of the water, transferring energy; the molecules of the water move up and down. A wave is a periodic disturbance of the water.

The top diagram represents the wave as an idealised **sine wave**. This idea can be used as a model for other phenomena:

- **Sound waves** travel through air (or any other medium). The particles of the medium vibrate back and forth as the wave travels along, as shown in the lower diagram.

- **Light** (and other **electromagnetic waves**) do not require a medium. They are a periodic disturbance of the electric and magnetic fields through which they are travelling. These fields vary at right angles to the direction of travel of the wave.

The wave travels horizontally

Molecules vibrate up and down (approximately)

Wave travelling horizontally

Particles vibrate back and forth

Compression   Rarefaction

Transverse and longitudinal waves

Transverse waves can be made to travel along a stretched rope, by moving one end up and down (or from side to side). Both types of wave can be demonstrated using a long spring: for longitudinal waves, the end of the spring must be pushed back and forth along the direction of motion; for transverse, it must be moved up and down or side to side, at right angles to the direction of motion. However, it is simplest to represent waves, transverse or longitudinal, as sine waves.

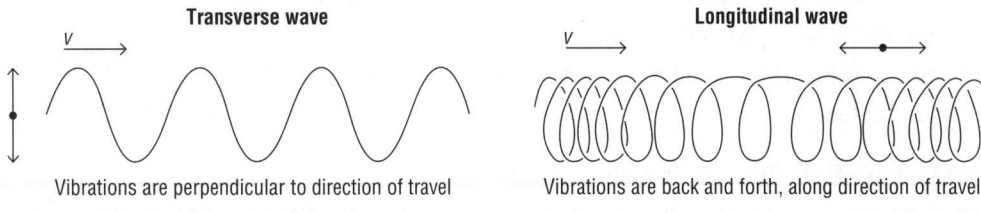

Transverse wave

Vibrations are perpendicular to direction of travel

Longitudinal wave

Vibrations are back and forth, along direction of travel

Wave fronts and rays

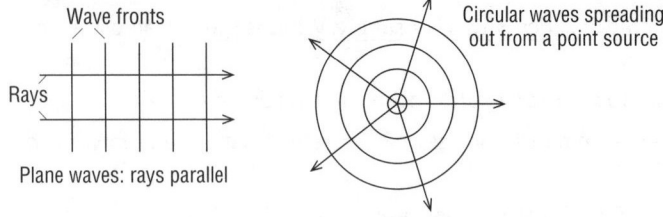

Wave fronts

Rays

Plane waves: rays parallel

Circular waves spreading out from a point source

The ripple tank shows another way to represent waves. We draw wave fronts as though we were looking down on the ripples from above.

We can add rays; these are always perpendicular to the wave front.

Note that the separation of the wave fronts is constant.

Reflection and refraction

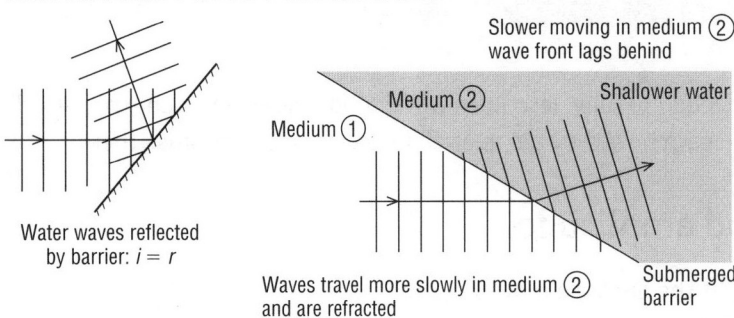

Water waves reflected by barrier: $i = r$

Slower moving in medium ② wave front lags behind

Shallower water

Medium ②

Medium ①

Waves travel more slowly in medium ② and are refracted

Submerged barrier

All waves can be reflected and refracted.

- **Reflection** occurs when a wave meets a barrier; part or all of the wave bounces off the barrier.

- **Refraction** occurs when a wave enters a medium in which it has a different speed. If it enters obliquely (not along the normal), it will change direction.

Changing wavelength

From the diagram on the right you can see that, when a wave enters a medium where it travels more slowly, its wavelength decreases. Its frequency remains constant.

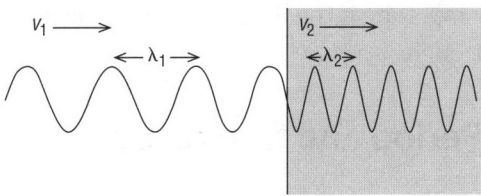

✓ *Quick check 3, 4*

Diffraction

All waves can be diffracted, another characteristic property of waves.

- **Diffraction** is the spreading out of a wave as it passes through a gap or around an object.

Notice that the wavelength (and frequency) of the diffracted wave are unchanged. The strongest diffraction effects occur when the wavelength of the wave is similar to the width of the gap through which the wave is passing.

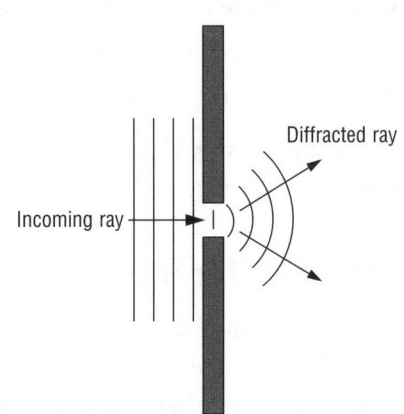

Diffracted ray

Incoming ray

Hint

More about diffraction on pages 59–61.

Module 4

QUICK CHECK QUESTIONS

1 Classify as transverse or longitudinal: light, sound, water, infrared waves.

2 A guitarist plucks a string. A wave travels along the string. Is this longitudinal or transverse?

3 Draw a ray diagram to show a single ray being reflected by a mirror placed at 45° to its path. Add wave fronts to show how these are reflected by the mirror.

4 Copy and complete the diagram below to show what happens when waves enter a medium where they travel more slowly. The boundary is parallel to the wave fronts.

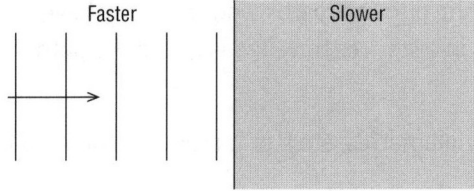

Faster

Slower

UNIT 2

Wave quantities

Key words

- amplitude
- wavelength
- period
- frequency
- phase

Examiner tip

You may be asked to take information from a drawing or graph of a wave. Note carefully whether the x-axis is distance or time, and look at the units.

✓ *Quick check 1*

Hint

Take care! The horizontal axis of this graph is *time*, not distance.

✓ *Quick check 2, 3*

✓ *Quick check 4–6*

Several quantities are needed to fully describe a wave: **amplitude**, **wavelength**, **period**, **frequency**, and **phase**. Learn how they are related; take care not to confuse them.

Wavelength and amplitude

- The **displacement** y is the distance moved by any particle from its undisturbed position.
- The **wavelength** λ (Greek letter lambda) of a wave is the distance between adjacent crests (or troughs), or between any two adjacent points that are at the same point in the cycle (i.e. that are **in phase** with each other).
- The **amplitude A** of a wave is the maximum displacement of any particle.

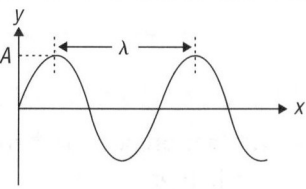

Horizontal axis = distance

Amplitude is the height of a crest measured from the horizontal axis, not from crest to trough.

Period and frequency

- The **period** T is the time for one complete cycle of the wave.
- This is related to the wave's **frequency** f: $T = 1/f$ (or $f = 1/T$).
- Frequency is measured in **hertz** (Hz). 1 Hz = 1 wave/s = 1 s^{-1}.
- 1 kHz = 10^3 Hz; 1 MHz = 10^6 Hz; 1 GHz = 10^9 Hz.

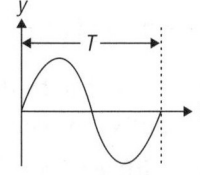

Think of it like this: the frequency is the number of waves per second; the period is the number of seconds per wave.

Phase difference

Two waves may have the same wavelength but be out of phase (out of step) with one another. Phase difference is expressed as a fraction of a cycle, or in **radians** (rad) or **degrees** (°).

- 1 cycle = 1 complete wave = 2π rad = 360°
- ½ cycle = π rad = 180°
- ¼ cycle = $\dfrac{\pi}{2}$ rad = 90°

Two waves in phase

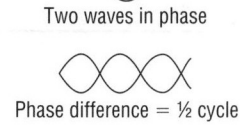

Phase difference = ½ cycle

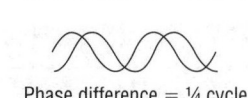

Phase difference = ¼ cycle

Similarly, there may be a phase difference between two points on the same wave.

- Points separated by one wavelength are in phase with each other.
- Points separated by half a wavelength have a phase difference of 180°.

Path difference

Two waves may arrive at the same point along different paths, and they may have travelled different distances. The difference in distances travelled is called the path difference.

Path difference may be given in metres (or millimetres, etc.), or it may be expressed in wavelengths.

Measuring frequency

To find the frequency of a sound wave, plug a microphone into an oscilloscope (c.r.o.) and use it to display the sound.

Hint

Check that the 'variable timebase' knob is in the 'calibrated' position.

■ WORKED EXAMPLE

STEP 1 Adjust the timebase setting to give two or three complete waves on the screen.
Timebase setting = 0.002 s div⁻¹ (2 ms per division)

STEP 2 Measure the width of a number of complete waves. Two waves occupy 5.0 divisions.

STEP 3 Calculate the time represented by this number of divisions.
Time = 5.0 div × 0.002 s div⁻¹ = 0.01 s

STEP 4 Calculate the frequency = number of waves/time.
Frequency = 2 waves/0.01 s = 200 Hz

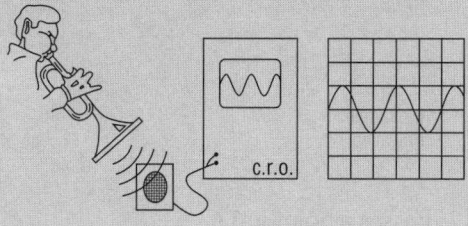

Hint

The timebase setting may be given in divisions or centimetres.

✔*Quick check 7*

Module 4

QUICK CHECK QUESTIONS

1 What quantities are represented by *p* and *q* in the diagram? What are their values?

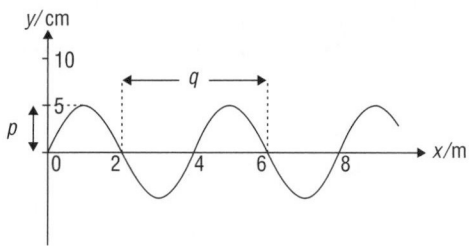

2 Calculate the period for waves of the following frequencies: 2 Hz, 2 kHz, 0.5 MHz.

3 What is the frequency of a wave whose period is 0.4 ms? Give your answer in kHz.

4 On the same axes, sketch two waves with a phase difference of π radians; one wave has twice the amplitude of the other.

5 A wave has a wavelength of 24 cm. Two points on the wave have a phase difference of 180°. What is the smallest possible separation between these points?

6 A sound wave has a wavelength of 100 cm. Two points on the wave are separated by 25 cm. What is the phase difference between them? Give your answer in degrees and in radians.

7 An oscilloscope is set with its timebase at 5 ms cm⁻¹. An alternating signal gives four complete waves across the 6 cm screen. What is the frequency of the signal?

Wave speed

Module 4

Key word

• progressive wave

Hint

The opposite of a progressive wave is a standing or stationary wave – see page 62.

Waves are one way in which energy is transferred from place to place. How quickly they do this depends on their speed, which may be anything up to c, the speed of light in free space, 3×10^8 m s^{-1}.

Speed, frequency and wavelength

The waves we have considered so far are described as **progressive waves**. They travel through space. The **speed v** of the wave tells us how fast it moves. The speed is the distance travelled per second by a crest.

Speed v is related to frequency f and wavelength λ by

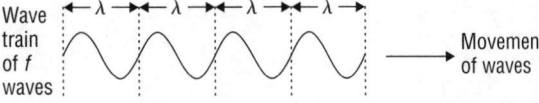

$$\text{speed} = \text{frequency} \times \text{wavelength} \qquad v = f\lambda$$

Deriving $v = f\lambda$

Wave train of f waves ⊣λ⊢λ⊢λ⊢λ⊢ ⟶ Movement of waves

- A 'train' of f waves, each of length λ, passes a point in 1 s.
- The total length of the train is $f\lambda$.
- This is the length of the waves passing per second, i.e. the speed v of the wave.

(You may find it easier to think in terms of numbers. A train of 4 waves passes a point in 1 s. Each wave is 5 m long. The total length of waves passing in 1 s is thus 4×5 m $= 20$ m, so the speed $v = 20$ m s^{-1}.)

A note on units

- Frequency f is in hertz (Hz).
- Wavelength λ is in metres (m).

Since 1 Hz $= 1$ s^{-1}, multiplying $f \times \lambda$ gives a result in m Hz, or m s^{-1}. This is the correct unit for speed.

✓ *Quick check 1, 2*

■ WORKED EXAMPLE 1

An observer, standing at the end of a pier, observes one wave passing by every 8 s. The distance between adjacent peaks is 12 m. Calculate the speed of the waves.

STEP 1 Calculate the frequency of the waves.

$$f = \frac{1}{8 \text{ s}} = 0.125 \text{ Hz}$$

STEP 2 Note down the wavelength of the waves.

$$\lambda = 12 \text{ m}$$

STEP 3 Calculate the wave speed.

$$\text{speed } v = f\lambda = 0.125 \text{ Hz} \times 12 \text{ m} = 1.5 \text{ m s}^{-1}$$

■ WORKED EXAMPLE 2

Calculate the wavelength of an electromagnetic wave (speed = 3×10^8 m s^{-1}) of frequency 100 GHz.

STEP 1 Write down quantities; convert to scientific notation (powers of 10).

$$v = 3 \times 10^8 \text{ m s}^{-1}, f = 100 \text{ GHz} = 100 \times 10^9 \text{ Hz}, \lambda = ?$$

STEP 2 Rearrange the equation, substitute values and solve.

$$\lambda = \frac{v}{f} = \frac{3 \times 10^8 \text{ m s}^{-1}}{100 \times 10^9 \text{ Hz}} = 3 \times 10^{-3} \text{ m}$$

Hint

Note that it is simplest to change units such as GHz to powers of 10; then enter them into your calculator in this form. You could give this answer as $\lambda = 3$ mm.

✓*Quick check 3–5*

Module 4

QUICK CHECK QUESTIONS

1 If some sound waves have a frequency of 200 Hz, how many will enter your ear in 1 s?

2 Some waves on the sea have a wavelength of 20 m. If three complete waves pass the end of the pier in one minute, what is the total length of the waves passing this point each minute?

3 Calculate the speed of ripples whose wavelength is 3 mm and whose frequency is 15 Hz.

4 Calculate the frequency of a sound wave if its wavelength in air is 11 mm.
(Speed of sound in air = 330 m s^{-1}.)

5 Calculate the wavelength of a sound wave of frequency 220 Hz.
(Speed of sound in air = 330 m s^{-1}.)

The electromagnetic spectrum

Module 4

A prism or diffraction grating can split white light up into the familiar **spectrum**, from red to violet. This spectrum shows all the wavelengths present in visible light, arranged from the longest wavelength (red) to the shortest (violet).

This is only part of a much wider spectrum of *electromagnetic radiation*.

The visible spectrum

The symbol for wavelength is the Greek letter λ (lambda) (see page 50).

The range of wavelengths of visible light is from 400 nm (violet) to 700 nm (red).

400 nm (nanometres) = 400×10^{-9} m = 4×10^{-7} m

It is useful to remember a typical value for the wavelength of visible light – say, $\lambda = 500$ nm.

Hint

These are only approximate values – it depends on your eyes!

✓ *Quick check 1*

Beyond the visible

Region of spectrum	Range of wavelengths (shortest to longest)
Gamma rays (γ-rays)	10^{-16} to 10^{-10} m
X-rays	10^{-13} to 10^{-8} m
Ultraviolet	10^{-8} m to 4×10^{-7} m (400 nm)
Visible	400 nm to 700 nm
Infrared	7×10^{-7} m (700 nm) to 10^{-3} m
Microwaves	10^{-3} m to 10^{-1} m
Radio waves	10^{-1} m to 10^{6} m or more

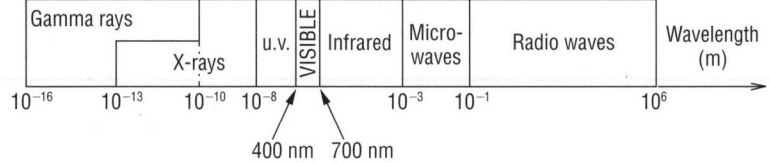

The electromagnetic spectrum includes wavelengths ranging over many orders of magnitude. It is divided into different regions, but the boundaries between them are not well defined.

You need to learn:

- the names of the different regions
- the order they appear in
- their approximate wavelength ranges.

The ultraviolet spectrum

The ultraviolet region of the electromagnetic spectrum is sub-divided into three parts:

UV-A is the longest wavelength (from 315 nm to 400 nm). This is the least hazardous, but over-exposure can cause burning and skin cancer.

UV-B and UV-C have progressively shorter wavelengths, and are more hazardous.

Sunscreen is used to block these rays so that they cannot penetrate the skin, causing cell damage and disrupting DNA.

Examiner tip

You should be able to consider applications of science and appreciate their benefits and risks.

✓ *Quick check 2, 3*

Speed of electromagnetic radiation

All types of electromagnetic radiation travel at the same speed through free space. This is often referred to as the **speed of light**, symbol c.

In the SI system of units, the value of c is defined as

$c = 299\ 792\ 458\ \text{m s}^{-1}$

This defines how metres and seconds are related in the SI system.

For many calculations, we can use an approximate value:

$c = 3 \times 10^8\ \text{m s}^{-1}$

Try to remember this approximate value.

> **Hint**
>
> 'Free space' means completely empty space – a perfect vacuum. Any material will slow electromagnetic radiation down.

> ✓ *Quick check 4, 5*

Practical uses of electromagnetic radiation

Gamma rays (γ-rays)	Medical: destroying cancerous tissue; imaging with tracers. Industrial: sterilising items that may be contaminated with microorganisms; seeing inside solid objects (similar to X-rays).
X-rays	Medical: imaging inside the body. Industrial: seeing inside solid objects, e.g. to detect cracks.
Ultraviolet	Medical: sterilisation; activating dental fillings. Industrial: sterilisation; visualising security markings. Consumer: reading DVDs.
Visible light	People: sight. Consumer: reading CDs.
Infrared	Consumer: remote controls, heating. Industrial: transmission via optical fibres.
Microwaves	Consumer: cooking. Industrial: telecommunications.
Radio waves	Medical: magnetic resonance imaging. Consumer: broadcasting, mobile phones. Industrial: communicating with spacecraft; telecommunications.

> **Examiner tip**
>
> You may be asked to describe some practical uses of electromagnetic waves.

Module 4

> **Hint**
>
> X-rays and γ-rays are very similar – we give them different names according to how they are produced.

QUICK CHECK QUESTIONS

1 The red limit of the visible spectrum is at about 700 nm. Express this in standard form, i.e. scientific notation, using powers of 10.

2 In what region of the electromagnetic spectrum does each of the following wavelengths lie? 1 km, 800 nm, 500 nm, 1 nm

3 Which section of the ultraviolet spectrum has the highest frequencies?

4 Which of the following give a good approximation to the speed of light in free space? 300 000 km s^{-1}, 300 000 000 m s^{-1}, 300 × 10^6 m s^{-1}

5 Roughly how many seconds does it take light to travel from the Sun to the Earth, a distance of 150 million km?

> **Hint**
>
> Try to answer question 2 without looking at the table of wavelengths.

Polarisation

Key words

- polarisation
- plane-polarised
- polarising filter
- intensity

Light is an electromagnetic wave. A light wave consists of varying electric and magnetic fields travelling through space. In light, as in all electromagnetic waves, the two fields vary at right-angles to each other.

In the diagram, the electric field is shown vibrating back and forth in the horizontal plane. This light would be described as **plane-polarised**. Most of the light we experience is unpolarised; that is, the waves are a mixture, with the electric field varying in all directions.

Magnetic (B) and electric (E) fields vibrate perpendicular to one another, and to the direction of travel

Only transverse waves can be polarised. Longitudinal waves have only one possible direction of vibration – back and forth, along the direction of propagation – so they cannot be polarised.

If a wave can be polarised, it must be transverse – that's how we know electromagnetic waves are transverse.

✓*Quick check 1, 2*

Module 4

Polarising filters

Passing unpolarised light through a polarising filter (a piece of Polaroid) selects out the waves that are plane-polarised in a particular plane, so that the light transmitted by the Polaroid is plane-polarised in a particular direction. Rotating the Polaroid changes the orientation of the polarised light.

After light has passed through one filter, it can be passed through a second filter that is oriented (has its axis) in the same direction.

If the second filter is at right angles to the first, the polarised light will be completely blocked. These are referred to as crossed polars; their axes are at 90° to each other.

✓*Quick check 3*

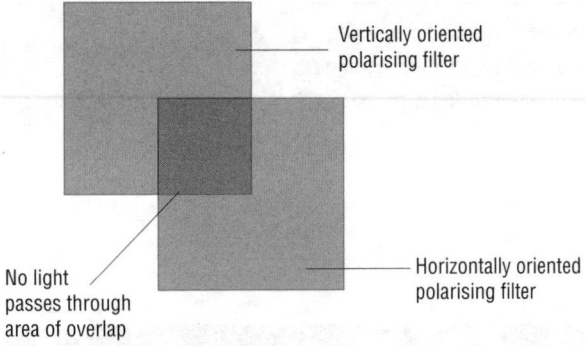

Vertically oriented polarising filter

No light passes through area of overlap

Horizontally oriented polarising filter

Reflected light

Although light from most everyday sources is unpolarised, light that has reflected off a surface is usually polarised (at least partially). For example, light may be reflected from the surface of a pond. The component whose electric field is varying in the horizontal plane will be reflected; the component at 90° to this will be refracted into the water.

Drivers may wear spectacles with Polaroid lenses, arranged so that the filters cut out this reflected light. This makes driving safer on wet roads as the driver is less likely to be blinded by reflected light.

Intensity and amplitude

Intensity I is a measure of the rate at which energy is transferred by a wave. It is the rate at which energy reaches a surface of area 1 m² at right angles to the direction of the wave. Units: watts per square metre (W m⁻²).

The greater the amplitude of a wave, the greater its intensity:

intensity $\propto$ (amplitude)² $I \propto A^2$

✓*Quick check 4*

Malus's law

The intensity of light passing through a polarising filter depends on the angle θ between the direction of polarisation of the light and the axis of the filter.

$$I = I_0 \cos^2 \theta$$

where I is the transmitted intensity and I_0 is the intensity before passing through the polarising filter.

✓*Quick check 5, 6*

This is because the electric vector of each photon may be resolved into a component parallel to the plane of polarisation, which is transmitted, and a component at right angles to it, which is absorbed.

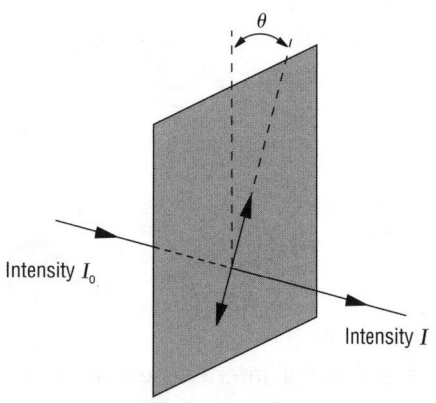

Intensity I_0

Intensity I

Module 4

QUICK CHECK QUESTIONS ❓

1 Can microwaves be polarised? Explain your answer.

2 Explain why sound waves cannot be polarised.

3 Unpolarised light is passed through one polarising filter and then through a second. The second filter has no effect on the intensity of the light.
   a What can you say about the orientation of the second filter?
   b If the second filter is rotated through 90°, what effect will this have on the transmitted light?

4 The amplitude of a wave doubles. By what factor has its intensity increased?

5 A beam of light of intensity 20 W m⁻² is incident on a polarising filter. The angle between the light's plane of polarisation is 45°. What is the intensity of the transmitted light?

6 The intensity of a beam of polarised light is reduced to 20% of its initial value when it passes through a polarising filter. Calculate the angle θ between the plane of polarisation and the axis of the filter.

Hint

Take care! First, calculate $I/I_0 = \cos^2 \theta$. Next, take the square root to find $\cos \theta$. Finally, deduce the angle.

Interference and diffraction

Module 4

Key words

- interference
- constructive
- destructive
- path difference
- coherent

✓ *Quick check 1*

What happens when two waves meet? Two snooker balls would bounce off one another, but waves behave differently. They show behaviour known as **interference**.

Constructive interference

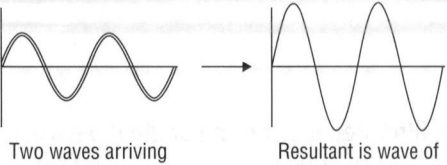

Two waves arriving in phase (in step) → Resultant is wave of twice the amplitude

Destructive interference

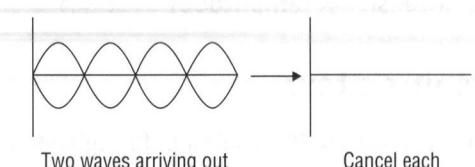

Two waves arriving out of phase (out of step) → Cancel each other out

- Two waves in phase add together to give a wave of a greater amplitude (equal to the sum of the two amplitudes). This is **constructive interference**.
- Two waves of the same amplitude and out of phase by 180° (half a wavelength) cancel out. This is **destructive interference**.

Interference of sound

Walking around in the space beyond the two loudspeakers, you can hear points where the sound is loud, and points where it is much softer. These loud and soft points have a regular pattern.

Your ear receives waves from both speakers. Suppose the wavelength of the sound waves is 1 m. If your ear is 4 m from one speaker and 5 m from the other, there is a **path difference** of 1 m for the two waves. They will be *in phase*; they will interfere constructively and you will hear a loud sound.

If your ear is 4 m from one speaker and 5.5 m from the other, the path difference is 1.5 m. The waves will be *out of phase*; they will interfere destructively and you will hear no sound (or a very faint sound).

- For constructive interference, path difference = $n\lambda$.
- For destructive interference, path difference = $(n + \frac{1}{2})\lambda$.

Examiner tip

You should be able to describe experiments that demonstrate interference for sound, light and microwaves.

✓ *Quick check 2*

Interference of other waves

The same effect can be shown for:

- *ripples* – use two dippers attached to a vibrating bar in a ripple tank
- *microwaves* – direct the microwaves through two gaps in a metal plate
- *light* – the 'Young's slits' experiment – see page 60.

Diffraction of ripples

Width of gap = x

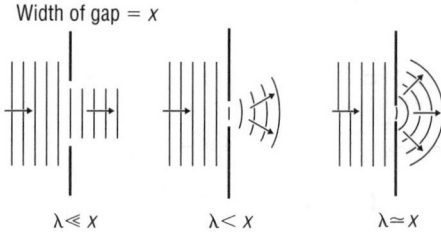

$\lambda \ll x$ $\lambda < x$ $\lambda \approx x$

When ripples pass through a gap, they spread out into the space beyond. The effect, which is known as **diffraction**, is greatest when the width of the gap x is similar to the wavelength of the ripples λ.

✓ *Quick check 3*

Explaining diffraction

When light from a laser is shone through a single slit, a **diffraction pattern** of light and dark bands (called *interference fringes*) is seen on the screen. We picture waves spreading out from all points in the slit. Each point on the screen receives waves from each point in the slit. These waves interfere.

- Where all the interfering waves cancel each other out, we see a dark fringe (*destructive* interference).
- Where all the interfering waves add up, we see a bright fringe (*constructive* interference).

Coherent sources

To make an interference pattern where two sets of waves overlap, the waves must be **coherent**. This means they must have the same wavelength and frequency; also, the phase difference between them must be constant.

The two loudspeakers in the diagram on page 58 are coherent sources. They are connected to the same signal generator, so they vibrate back and forth in step with each other.

Light from a lamp is not usually coherent. The waves it emits do not keep in step with one another. Laser light is coherent; its waves remain in step between source and screen.

Module 4

Examiner tip

Don't write 'coherent sources must be in phase' – they can have a phase difference so long as it stays constant.

✓ *Quick check 4*

QUICK CHECK QUESTIONS

1 What will be observed if two waves, in phase with each other and one having twice the amplitude of the other, interfere?

2 Two sound waves of wavelength 40 cm leave two loudspeakers in phase with each other. They reach your ear at the same time. One wave has travelled 300 cm; the other 240 cm. What is the path difference between them? Give your answer in cm and in wavelengths. How will they interfere with each other?

3 Draw a ripple diagram (like those at the top of this page) to show ripples of wavelength λ being diffracted by a gap of width 2λ. Draw a second diagram to show what happens if ripples of twice this wavelength pass through the same gap.

4 Two dippers are used to produce an interference pattern in a ripple tank. Are they a pair of coherent sources? Explain your answer.

Key words

- Young's slits
- diffraction grating

Light shows interference. To produce two rays, light is shone through a pair of parallel slits. The light is diffracted by the slits; where it falls on a screen beyond the slits, light and dark interference 'fringes' are seen. This is known as Young's double-slit experiment.

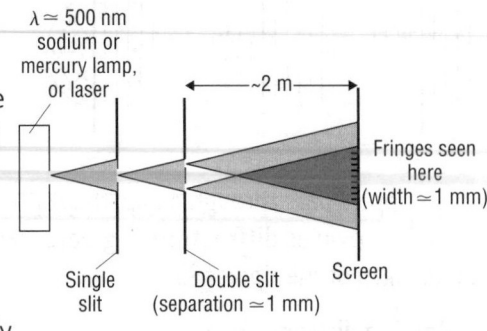

- The single slit acts as a narrow source of light, shining on the double slit. Alternatively, a laser can be shone directly on the double slit.

- As light passes through each slit, it spreads out into the space beyond. This is *diffraction* – see page 49.

✓*Quick check 1, 2*

- The fringe separation can be measured using a travelling microscope. Increasing the slit-to-screen distance makes the fringes wider but dimmer.

Explaining the interference fringes

Each point on the screen receives light waves from both slits (S_1 and S_2).

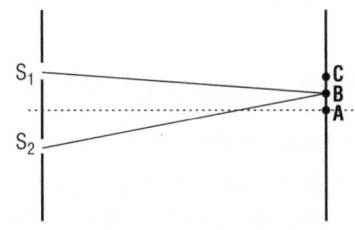

- **A** is directly opposite the point midway between the two slits. Waves leaving the two slits in phase with one another arrive at point **A** in phase. They interfere constructively and a bright fringe is seen. Path difference = 0.

- **B** is the centre of the first dark fringe. Waves from S_1 have a shorter distance to travel than waves from S_2. They arrive out of phase and interfere destructively. Path difference = $\lambda/2$.

- **C** is the centre of the next bright fringe. The two waves arrive in phase, but one has travelled further than the other. Path difference = λ.

Therefore:

- A bright fringe is seen where the two waves arrive in phase; path difference = $n\lambda$.

✓*Quick check 3*

- A dark fringe is seen where they arrive out of phase; path difference = $(n + \frac{1}{2})\lambda$.

Hint

You may find it easier to remember the formula as $\lambda D = ax$: largest quantity (D) times smallest (λ) equals the other two multiplied together.

Measuring the wavelength of light

The Young's slits experiment provides a method for determining λ, which is related to the screen distance D, slit separation a and fringe width x by:

$$\lambda = ax/D$$

✓*Quick check 4*

Note that, for white light, this can only give an average value of λ since many wavelengths are present. Laser light is monochromatic (a single wavelength) so the fringes are clearer and a more accurate value of λ can be found.

■ WORKED EXAMPLE

Laser light of wavelength 648 nm falls on a pair of slits separated by 1.5 mm. What will be the separation of the interference fringes seen on a screen 4.5 m from the slits?

STEP 1 Write down what you know, and what you want to know:
λ = 648 nm, a = 1.5 mm, D = 4.5 m, x = ?

STEP 2 Rearrange the equation, substitute values and solve:
$$x = \frac{\lambda D}{a} = \frac{648 \times 10^{-9}\,\text{m} \times 4.5\,\text{m}}{1.5 \times 10^{-3}\,\text{m}} = 1.9 \times 10^{-3}\,\text{m}$$

So the fringe width seen on the screen will be 1.9 mm.

✓*Quick check 5*

Diffraction gratings

A diffraction grating has many equally spaced parallel slits. Light waves from every slit must be in phase to produce a bright fringe. Fringes appear at angles θ according to:

$$d \sin \theta = n\lambda$$

where d is the separation of adjacent slits and n is an integer (0, ±1, ±2, etc).

Because it has many slits, a diffraction grating has the advantage that the bright fringes are more widely separated than for a double-slit arrangement, allowing for more precise measurement.

✓*Quick check 6*

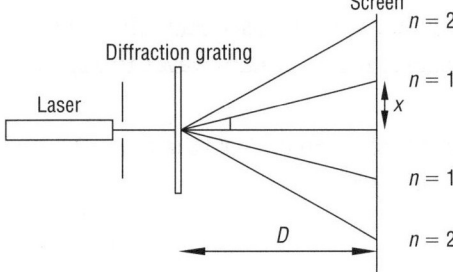

QUICK CHECK QUESTIONS

1 Give the symbol and approximate size for each of the following in the Young's slits experiment: slit-to-screen distance; slit separation; fringe separation; wavelength of light.

2 Look at the diagram of the experiment (top of opposite page). What part does diffraction play?

3 What can you say about the path difference between two waves which show destructive interference?

4 If the slit separation a is doubled, how will the fringe width x be changed?

5 White light is directed onto a pair of slits separated by 1.0 mm. Interference fringes are observed on a screen at a distance of 1.8 m. Five fringes have a width of 5.0 mm. Estimate the wavelength of the light. Why is your answer an estimate?

6 Light of wavelength 600 nm falls normally on a diffraction grating which has 200 lines per centimetre. At what angle will the first-order bright fringe (n = 1) be formed?

Hint

First calculate d; then calculate $\sin \theta$ and hence θ.

UNIT 2

Superposition and stationary waves

Key words

- superposition
- stationary wave
- node
- antinode

When two or more waves meet, the result is found by the **principle of superposition**. At any instant, the resultant displacement is simply the sum of the displacements of the individual waves. Constructive and destructive interference are obvious examples of this idea. It also explains the formation of **stationary waves**.

Stationary waves on a stretched string

The vibrator sends waves along the string. They reflect at the other end. The outgoing and reflected waves then interfere. At certain frequencies, a **stationary wave** (or standing wave) pattern of loops is formed.

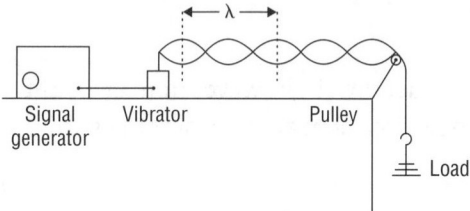

- At certain points – **nodes** – the two waves interfere destructively. There is no vibration. There are nodes at the ends of the string.

- Halfway between the nodes are **antinodes**. The string vibrates with a large amplitude. When the vibration has its maximum amplitude, the two waves are interfering constructively.

- Changing the frequency slightly causes the standing wave to disappear. Changing the length, tension or thickness of the string causes the stationary waves to appear at different frequencies.

- The wavelength of the wave is *twice* the distance from one node to the next; separation between adjacent nodes (or antinodes) = $\lambda/2$.

✓ *Quick check 1*

Conditions for a stationary wave

Two identical but oppositely travelling waves interfere with each other to form a stationary wave. Identical means that they have the same wavelength, frequency and amplitude. Often, one wave is a reflection of the other. For example, when microwaves are reflected by a metal plate, a standing wave pattern is formed.

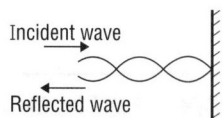

✓ *Quick check 2*

Using the principle of superposition

The diagrams show the two waves that make a stationary wave. They are shown at three instants in time. You can see that the waves are progressive waves, travelling in opposite directions.

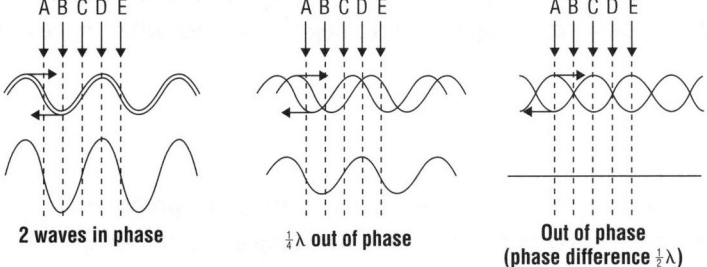

| 2 waves in phase | $\frac{1}{4}\lambda$ out of phase | Out of phase (phase difference $\frac{1}{2}\lambda$) |

Below these waves in the diagram are the resultant waves. These are worked out by adding the displacements of the two progressive waves.

- Points A, C and E are nodes; the two waves always cancel here.
- Points B and D are antinodes; the displacement here varies up and down.

✓ *Quick check 3*

Air columns

The diagram on the right shows a hollow tube with one end in water. When the frequency of the loudspeaker is changed, a point is reached where the note becomes much louder. Sound waves are reflected by the water and a standing wave has formed in the air column inside the cylinder. There is a node at the foot of the air column and an antinode at the top.

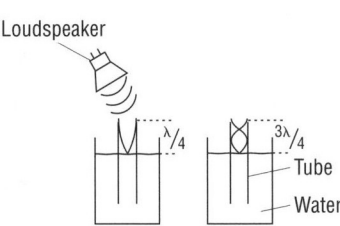

Loudspeaker
Tube
Water

At the lowest frequency at which this occurs (called the fundamental), the length of the air column is one-quarter of the wavelength of the sound. A stationary wave is formed again at three times this frequency, with three-quarters of a wave fitting in the column. This is the third harmonic of the fundamental. If you know the wavelength and the frequency, you can calculate the speed of sound using $v = f\lambda$.

✓ *Quick check 4*

In a tube open at both ends, a standing wave can still form, but with an antinode at each end.

Microwaves

To observe a stationary wave pattern with microwaves, direct microwaves at a vertical metal plate. Reflected waves interfere with incoming waves to form a standing wave pattern. Detect nodes (zero intensity) and antinodes (high intensity) between source and plate.

QUICK CHECK QUESTIONS

1   A string of length 1.2 m is stretched and vibrated so that a standing wave consisting of two loops is formed. Sketch this, and calculate the wavelength of the waves on the string.

2   Microwaves are directed at a sheet of steel. A detector is used to investigate the intensity of the waves between the source and the plate. A pattern of high and low intensity regions is found; the separation of adjacent high intensity regions is 1.5 cm. What is the wavelength of the microwaves?

3   Explain why there is a node at point C in the diagram at the top of this page.

4   In a vibrating air column experiment, the air column is 20 cm long. The lowest frequency that produces a standing wave is 400 Hz. Calculate the wavelength and speed of the sound waves.

Module 4

Examiner tip

'Sketch' means that a simple freehand drawing is acceptable. Nevertheless, you should take care over the proportions, and show important details.

UNIT 2 Photons

Sometimes we think of light as being made up of 'particles' called **photons**, each with its own energy. A photon is a **quantum** of energy of electromagnetic radiation. Sometimes we think of light as being made up of electromagnetic waves, which have a frequency and wavelength.

Wave frequency

The **frequency** of a wave is the number of wavecrests passing any given point per second. Frequency is measured in **hertz** (Hz); 1 Hz = 1 s⁻¹. The longer the wavelength, the lower the frequency.

Energy and frequency

The energy of a photon is related to the wave frequency f by

> **photon energy = hf**

where h is a constant known as the **Planck constant**: $h = 6.63 \times 10^{-34}$ J s.

You can think of the units J s as 'joules per hertz'. The more hertz (the higher the frequency), the more joules are carried by each photon.

This equation links a particle property (photon energy) to a wave property (frequency). Since frequency and wavelength are related to the speed of light c by $c = f\lambda$, we can write:

> **photon energy** $= \dfrac{hc}{\lambda}$

The electronvolt – an energy unit

Photon energies are very small. A more convenient unit than the joule is the **electronvolt** (eV).

1 eV is the energy transferred when an electron moves between two points separated by a p.d. of 1 V.

> **1 eV = 1.6 × 10⁻¹⁹ J**

- To convert from J to eV: divide by 1.6×10^{-19} (i.e. multiply by 6.25×10^{18}).
- To convert from eV to J: multiply by 1.6×10^{-19}.

Key words

- Planck constant
- electronvolt
- de Broglie equation

Hint

For more details of this relationship, see page XX.

✓ *Quick check 1, 2*

Hint

Remember the equation $W = QV$ (energy = charge × voltage) on page 36. That's where the definition of the electronvolt comes from. The electron charge is $e = 1.6 \times 10^{-19}$ C.

✓ *Quick check 3–5*

Module 5

The de Broglie equation

$E = hf$ is one equation that links a wave property (frequency f) with a particle property (photon energy E). The **de Broglie equation** is another equation that allows us to translate between wave behaviour and particle behaviour. It links wavelength λ with particle momentum mv. The more momentum a particle has, the shorter its wavelength:

$$\lambda = \frac{h}{mv}$$

Note that, in both of these equations, the Planck constant h connects the wave quantity to the particle quantity.

A note on momentum

You can calculate momentum by multiplying mass by velocity, $m \times v$. The greater the mass of a particle, and the faster it moves, the greater its momentum. The units of momentum are kg m s^{-1} or N s.

Hint

You will find lots more on momentum in Unit 1 of the companion book – Revise A2 Physics for OCR, Specification A.

■ WORKED EXAMPLE

An electron has momentum 2×10^{-24} kg m s^{-1}. What is its wavelength?

$$\lambda = \frac{h}{mv} = \frac{6.63 \times 10^{-34} \text{ J s}}{2 \times 10^{-24} \text{ kg m s}^{-1}} = 3.31 \times 10^{-10} \text{ m}$$

(This value of momentum is for an electron moving at roughly 2×10^{6} m s^{-1}. Its wavelength is similar to the size of an atom, which is why such electrons are diffracted by crystalline graphite – see page 68.)

The de Broglie equation applies to *all* particles, no matter how big. If you run, you are like a moving particle. Your momentum might be 500 kg m s^{-1}; your wavelength would then be about 10^{-32} m. This is much too small for you to observe any wave effects, such as diffraction or interference.

✓*Quick check 6*

Module 5

QUICK CHECK QUESTIONS ❓

1 Calculate the energy of each photon in a beam of light of frequency 5.0×10^{14} Hz.

2 Red light has a wavelength of 700 nm. Calculate the energy of a photon of red light.

3 How many electronvolts of energy are transformed when an electron moves through a p.d. of 10.5 V?

Hint

Use your answer to question 1 above.

4 What is the energy in eV of each photon in a beam of light of frequency 5.0×10^{14} Hz?

5 A laser produces photons of energy 1.90 eV. What is the wavelength of the laser light?

6 Light has momentum. Each photon in a beam of light carries an amount of momentum which can be calculated using the de Broglie equation. For light of wavelength 700 nm, what is the momentum of each photon?

Hint

(Planck constant $h = 6.63 \times 10^{-34}$ J s, speed of light in free space = 3.0×10^{8} m s^{-1}.)

The photoelectric effect

Key words

- photoelectric effect
- photocell
- work function
- threshold frequency

Hint

I in the figure is conventional current. Electrons move in the opposite direction.

✓*Quick check 1*

When ultraviolet radiation shines on certain metals, electrons break free. This is the **photoelectric effect**.

In order to explain this effect, Albert Einstein had to assume that, when light interacts with a metal, it behaves as particles (photons), not as waves. The energy of a photon of light is captured by a *conduction electron* in the metal, and the electron escapes from the surface of the metal.

Observing the photoelectric effect

When electromagnetic radiation of sufficiently high energy is shone onto the **photocell**, a current starts to flow immediately. Even a very feeble light will work. The brighter the ultraviolet light, the greater the current.

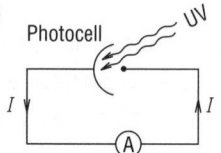

The explanation is that the energy of the light helps conduction electrons to break free from the metal cathode. They cross to the anode; now there is a flow of charge all round the circuit. More light means more energy, so more electrons break free.

Explaining the photoelectric effect

Electrons don't normally escape from a metal. The conduction electrons are weakly held inside the metal. They need some energy to escape. Light can provide the necessary energy.

Why waves can't explain the effect

If we picture light waves falling on the metal, their energy is spread out all over the surface of the metal. It would take a long time for enough energy to be captured by the metal to free any electrons. The photoelectric effect is surprising because electrons break free as soon as the light is switched on.

Einstein argued that the energy of the light must be concentrated in tiny packets (photons). An individual conduction electron in the metal captures an individual photon; now the electron has enough energy to escape from the metal.

In the figure,

- hf is the energy of the photon
- KE is the kinetic energy of the electron
- ϕ is the **work function** of the metal – the least amount of energy needed for an electron to escape from the metal.

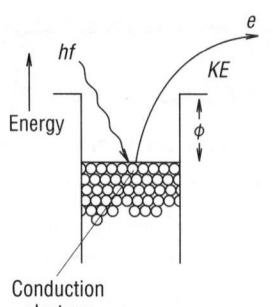

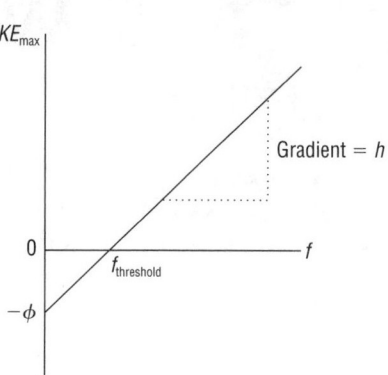

The gradient of a graph of KE_{max} against f gives the Planck constant h. The intercept gives work function ϕ.

How photons explain the effect

If a photon is captured by an electron in the metal, some of its energy is used to overcome the work function, and the rest ends up as the electron's kinetic energy. The electrons that are highest up in the energy 'well' are the most energetic electrons. When one of these electrons captures a photon and escapes, it will have the maximum possible kinetic energy, KE_{max}. This gives us the equation:

$$hf = \phi + KE_{max}$$

Brighter light means more photons, so more electrons released. However, this doesn't increase the KE of the fastest electrons, because the individual photons do not have more energy. The current produced is proportional to the intensity of the light; greater intensity means more photons per second, so more electrons are released per second.

Threshold frequency

The frequency of the light must be above a certain minimum value, the **threshold frequency** $f_{threshold}$. Below this value, an individual photon does not have enough energy for an electron to overcome the work function. Hence:

$$hf_{threshold} = \phi$$

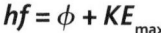 *Quick check 2, 3*

■ WORKED EXAMPLE

A metal has a work function $\phi = 0.8$ eV. What is the greatest possible kinetic energy of an electron released by a photon of energy 1.4 eV?

Of the 1.4 eV of energy provided by the photon, 0.8 eV is used up in overcoming the work function. This leaves 0.6 eV of kinetic energy.

$$KE_{max} = 1.4 \text{ eV} - 0.8 \text{ eV} = 0.6 \text{ eV}$$

(It is easiest to work in eV. However, you might have to calculate the photon energy from its frequency, and you might have to calculate the maximum speed of the electron using ½ mv^2.)

Quick check 4

QUICK CHECK QUESTIONS

1   A photocell makes a current flow around a circuit. Is the voltage across it a p.d. or an e.m.f.? Does the current *inside* the photocell flow from + to –, or from – to +?

2   What is the threshold frequency for a metal surface whose work function is 2.4×10^{-19} J?

3   Photons of energy 3.0 eV fall on a surface whose work function is 1.8 eV. What is the maximum kinetic energy of electrons emitted? (Give your answer in eV.)

Hint

Question 3 is simple if you work in eV.

4   Light of frequency 3.0×10^{14} Hz falls on a metal surface whose work function is 1.0 eV. What is the speed of the fastest electrons released?

Hint

In question 4, it is probably easiest to work in joules, rather than eV.
Do not mix J and eV.

Hint

(Planck constant $h = 6.63 \times 10^{-34}$ J s, electron mass $m_e = 9.1 \times 10^{-31}$ kg, electron charge $e = 1.6 \times 10^{-19}$ C.)

Module 5

Wave–particle duality

UNIT 2

Module 5

Key words

- wave–particle duality
- electron diffraction

For Einstein to explain the photoelectric effect, he had to assume that, when light interacts with the conduction electrons in a metal, it behaves as particles (photons). At other times, we know that light behaves as waves – for example, when it is diffracted (spread out) as it passes through a slit, or when two light waves interfere with one another. So light can behave as waves or as particles, depending on the circumstances. This is known as **wave–particle duality**.

In a similar way, particles (such as electrons) may also show wave-like behaviour.

Electron diffraction

Electrons can be diffracted. This shows that, when they pass through a fine grid, they behave like waves.

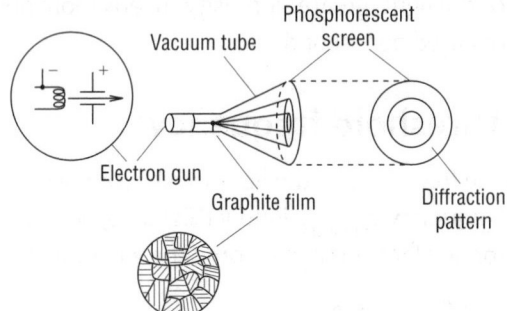

- A beam of fast-moving electrons is produced in a cathode ray tube.

- The electron beam passes through a thin layer of crystalline graphite (carbon).

- A diffraction pattern of fuzzy, light-and-dark rings is produced on a screen.

- To make the electrons go faster, increase the accelerating voltage. The diameter of the rings decreases. This shows that the wavelength decreases as the electrons go faster.

You can imagine how, as the wavelength of the waves gets smaller and smaller, the waves pass more easily through the gaps between the layers of carbon atoms, so they are diffracted less. From the degree to which electrons are diffracted, the arrangement and separation of atoms in solids can be found. The diffraction of higher energy electrons can be used to determine the size of atomic nuclei.

✓ *Quick check 1, 2*

Accelerating electrons

Note that we can find the kinetic energy of an electron if we know the voltage through which it has been accelerated using:

$$eV = \tfrac{1}{2} mv^2$$

This equation says that the energy gained by the electron when it is accelerated through voltage V is eV, and this is its kinetic energy E_k. The equation can be used for any charged particles, including protons (charge $+e$) and ions. A proton accelerated through 5000 V will have KE of 5 keV or $5000 \times 1.6 \times 10^{-19}$ J $= 8.0 \times 10^{-16}$ J.

Electrons accelerated through much higher voltages have very short wavelengths. This means that they are diffracted by atomic nuclei, and so can be used to determine the dimensions of the nucleus.

✓ *Quick check 3, 4*

Module 5

■ WORKED EXAMPLE

An electron accelerated through 100 V has momentum approximately equal to 5.4×10^{-24} kg m s⁻¹. Calculate the wavelength of such an electron and compare it to the separation of carbon atoms in graphite, approximately 0.37 nm.

STEP 1 Use the de Broglie equation to calculate the electron's wavelength.
$$\lambda = \frac{h}{mv} = \frac{6.63 \times 10^{-34} \text{ J s}}{5.4 \times 10^{-24} \text{ kg m s}^{-1}} = 1.2 \times 10^{-10} \text{ m}$$

STEP 2 Compare with the separation of carbon atoms in graphite = 0.37 nm = 3.7×10^{-10} m.

The electron's de Broglie wavelength is about one-third of the atomic separation, so significant diffraction will be observed.

✓*Quick check 5*

Waves or particles?

So, is light made up of waves or particles? Are electrons waves or particles? The answer is as follows.

We cannot say that light is waves, or particles. Sometimes light *behaves like* waves, sometimes it *behaves like* particles. And the same is true for electrons (and any other particle). We just have to learn when the wave picture gives the better explanation, and when the particle picture is better.

Waves and particles are things we are familiar with in our everyday lives. On the microscopic scale of electrons and photons, we discover that matter and radiation behave in a way that is a strange mixture of the two. We simply have to learn when to apply the wave picture or model, and when to think in terms of particles.

Some people try to invent funny little pictures of 'wavicles', half-wave and half-particle. This doesn't really help; it's best just to use either the wave model or the particle model, as appropriate.

✓*Quick check 6*

Measuring the Planck constant *h*

Connect an LED to a power supply; connect a voltmeter across the LED. Gradually turn up the voltage until the LED starts to light up; note the voltage. Repeat with LEDs of different colours; find out the wavelength λ of each LED.

We have $eV = hc/\lambda$; a graph of V against $1/\lambda$ will have a gradient of e/hc, from which h can be deduced.

QUICK CHECK QUESTIONS

1   In a diffraction experiment, what would happen to the speed of the electrons if the accelerating voltage was decreased? How would the diffraction pattern change?

2   In Einstein's explanation of the photoelectric effect, do the electrons behave as particles or as waves?

3   An electron, charge $e = 1.6 \times 10^{-19}$ C, is accelerated through 2.0 kV. What is its KE in eV, and in J?

4   Electrons used to measure the dimensions of an atomic nucleus must be accelerated through a much higher voltage than those used to measure interatomic spacings. Explain why this is.

5   A proton has momentum 1.5×10^{-18} kg m s⁻¹. Calculate its de Broglie wavelength. How does this compare with the diameter of a typical nucleus (10^{-15} m)?

6   Calculate the de Broglie wavelength for a car of mass 500 kg travelling at 20 m s⁻¹. Use your answer to explain why cars don't exhibit wave-like behaviour.

Module 5

Key words

- emission spectrum
- energy level

Hint

If you are studying Chemistry, you will know that an element can be identified from the wavelengths present in its line spectrum.

When a gas is heated, it glows. If the light is passed through a diffraction grating or prism, a spectrum is formed. The spectrum consists of a number of discrete lines, showing that only certain wavelengths are present.

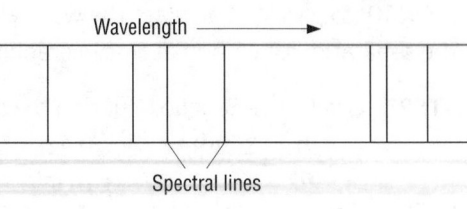

Wavelength ⟶

Spectral lines

This is an **emission line spectrum**, so called because it arises from light emitted by a material.

If white light is passed through a hot gas, black lines appear in its spectrum. This absorption line spectrum shows that certain wavelengths have been absorbed.

Energy levels

The explanation of line spectra is based on the arrangement of electrons in an atom. In an atom, electrons can only occupy a number of discrete energy levels. (The word *discrete* means *separate* or *distinct*.) The diagram shows a typical arrangement of energy levels.

On this diagram, the vertical axis is a scale of electron energy E. The horizontal lines indicate the different permitted energy levels. The dots represent electrons occupying the different levels.

✓*Quick check 1*

Notice that the energy scale usually starts with $E = 0$ at the top. Energies can be given in J or eV.

E/eV

```
0
−1.0
−3.0
−5.0
−8.0
−12.0
```

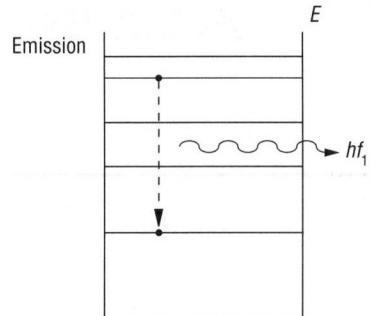

Emission

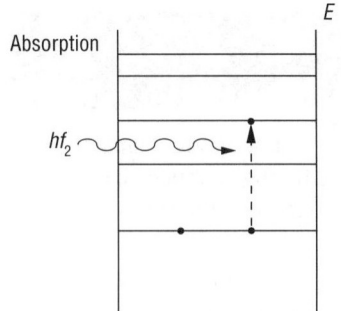

Absorption

Changing energy

When an electron loses energy, it moves downwards, from one level to another. In doing so, it emits a single photon whose energy corresponds *exactly* to the difference between the two levels. So, for an electron falling from level E_1 to E_2, the photon must have energy hf given by:

$$hf = E_1 - E_2$$

Similarly, when an electron gains energy, it moves upwards from one level to another. It can only do this by *absorbing* a photon whose energy corresponds *exactly* to the difference between the two levels; there can be no energy left over. The same equation gives the energy of the photon.

In the diagrams, the photons are represented by wavy lines and the symbol hf.

Since the energy of a photon can also be written in terms of its wavelength λ, we can also write:

$$\frac{hc}{\lambda} = E_1 - E_2$$

■ WORKED EXAMPLE

An electron loses energy when it falls from a level where its energy is –5.0 eV to a lower level, energy –12.7 eV. Calculate the frequency and wavelength of the photon emitted.

STEP 1 Calculate the energy of the photon, in eV:
$$E_1 - E_2 = -5.0 - (-12.7) = +7.7 \text{ eV}$$
STEP 2 Convert this energy to joules:
$$\text{Energy} = 7.7 \times 1.6 \times 10^{-19} = 12.3 \times 10^{-19} \text{ J}$$
STEP 3 Calculate the frequency of the photon:
$$f = E/h = 12.3 \times 10^{-19}/6.63 \times 10^{-34} = 1.86 \times 10^{15} \text{ Hz}$$
STEP 4 Calculate the wavelength of the photon:
$$\lambda = c/f = 3.0 \times 10^8/1.86 \times 10^{15} = 1.62 \times 10^{-7} \text{ m}$$

✔ *Quick check 2–4*

Explaining spectra

The fact that the energy levels in isolated atoms are discrete explains why we see line spectra. The photons of each line have energies that correspond to the gap between two energy levels.

- In an emission spectrum, electrons are 'falling' from higher levels to lower levels, emitting photons.

- In an absorption spectrum, electrons are 'jumping up' from lower levels to higher levels, absorbing photons as they do so.

Once the wavelengths present in a line spectrum have been measured, it is possible to work out the energy level diagram of the atoms producing the spectrum.

✔ *Quick check 5*

Module 5

QUICK CHECK QUESTIONS

1 Look at the first energy level diagram on the opposite page. Which energy levels are occupied?

2 Look again at the first energy level diagram on the opposite page. If an electron moves from the –8.0 eV level to the –3.0 eV level, does this involve emission or absorption of a photon? Calculate the energy of the photon in eV.

3 An electron moves from an energy level –20.4 eV to a higher level of energy –10.8 eV. Calculate the frequency of the photon it absorbs to make this transition possible.

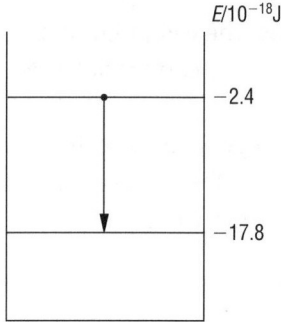

Hint

(Planck constant $h = 6.63 \times 10^{-34}$ J s, speed of light in free space = 3.0×10^8 m s^{-1}, electron charge $e = 1.6 \times 10^{-19}$ C.)

4 The energy level diagram above shows an electron falling from one energy level to another. Calculate the wavelength of the photon emitted in this process.

5 For the first energy level diagram on the opposite page, explain why a photon of energy 4.8 eV could not be absorbed by such an atom.

End-of-unit questions

See Appendix 3 on page 79 for data and equations provided in the examination.

Modules 1–3: Electricity

1 A 12 Ω resistor is connected in a circuit with a 3 V battery of negligible internal resistance.

   a Draw a circuit diagram to show this circuit. Add arrows to indicate the directions of conventional current flow, and of electron flow.

   b Calculate the current in the circuit. How much charge flows through the resistor each second?

   c What is the potential difference across the resistor?

   d Calculate the energy transferred in the resistor each second.

2 **a** Write down an equation linking charge, energy and potential difference. Explain how this equation is used to define potential difference.

   b Use your answer to part **a** to define the volt.

   c The electromotive force (e.m.f.) of a cell can be defined as 'the energy transferred per unit charge when the cell pushes 1 coulomb of charge around a circuit'. Explain how this definition is related to the equation you have stated in part **a**.

3 In the diagram, a resistor R and a thermistor T are connected to a cell of negligible internal resistance.

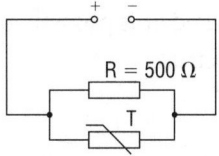

   a Are the two resistors R and T connected in series or in parallel with one another?

   b A current of 10 mA flows through the resistor R. Calculate the p.d. across it.

   c A current of 4 mA flows through T. What is its resistance?

   d The thermistor T is heated so that its resistance decreases. Will the current through it increase, decrease or stay the same?

   e Will the current through R increase, decrease or stay the same?

4 In an experiment to investigate the resistance of an alloy of copper, some students use a 0.56 m length of copper alloy wire of diameter 0.40 mm.

   a Calculate the resistance of the wire at room temperature. (Resistivity of the copper alloy at room temperature = 3.4×10^{-7} Ω m.)

The students find that, when a p.d. of 6.0 V is applied across the wire, a current of 4.0 A flows through it. Doubling the p.d. to 12.0 V results in a current of 6.9 A. They notice that the wire is now hot.

   b Sketch a current–voltage characteristic graph for the copper alloy wire, to show the results that you would expect the students to obtain if they measured current and voltage over a greater range of values. State and explain whether or not the copper alloy wire is an ohmic conductor.

5 A battery of e.m.f. 12.0 V and internal resistance 2.0 Ω is connected as shown to two 5.0 Ω resistors.

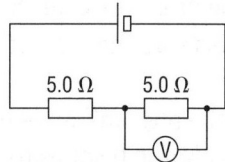

   a Calculate the potential difference measured by the high-impedance voltmeter V.
   b Calculate the terminal p.d. across the battery.
   c Explain why the battery's terminal p.d. would increase if the two resistors were replaced with resistors each of value 5 kΩ.

6 In normal use, a 150 W lamp is found to draw a current of 1.5 A from a supply.
   a Calculate the resistance of the lamp when it is in use.
   b If the lamp is left switched on for 24 hours, how many kWh of energy are transferred?

Module 4: Waves

7 Sound waves from a vibrating transducer are transmitted along a steel rail. Their speed in the steel is 6000 m s^{-1}.
   a The frequency of the vibrations is 50 kHz. Calculate their wavelength in the steel.
   b If the frequency of the vibrations is decreased, how will their wavelength be affected?

8 You are provided with a microwave generator, two metal plates, and a microwave detector. Describe how you would demonstrate the diffraction of microwaves using this equipment.

9 Laser light of wavelength 648 nm is passed through a pair of parallel slits; on a screen 5.7 m away, a pattern of light and dark fringes is seen.
   a Using the terms *constructive interference* and *path difference*, explain how a bright fringe is formed.
   b The width of 10 of the fringes is found to be 2.8 cm. Calculate the separation of the two slits.

10 Here are three types of wave:
light waves   microwaves   sound waves
   a Which of these are longitudinal waves?
   b Which of these can be polarised?

11 Stationary waves can be created by plucking a stretched string.
   a With the aid of a diagram, explain what is meant by a node and an antinode.
   b Explain how such a standing wave is formed when the string is plucked.

12 A string is stretched horizontally. One end is moved up and down at a frequency of 30 Hz, so that a train of waves travels along the string. The wavelength of these waves is found to be 4 cm.
   a Are these waves longitudinal or transverse? Explain your answer.
   b Calculate the velocity of the waves.
   c When the waves reflect from the other end of the string, a standing wave pattern is formed. What is the separation of adjacent nodes in this pattern?

Module 5: Quantum physics

13 a A student wrote 'All members of the electromagnetic spectrum travel at the same speed, approximately 3×10^8 m s^{-1}.' Explain how this statement must be modified to make it correct.

    b An atom emits a photon of energy 4×10^{-19} J. Calculate the photon's wavelength.

    c State which region of the electromagnetic spectrum the photon belongs to.

Examiner tip

In **b** you are asked to 'show that . . .'. In an examination, marks will be awarded for showing all the steps in the calculation. If you cannot do this part of the question, you can still attempt part **d** using the value for photon energy that you are given in **b**.

14 In an experiment to measure the work function of potassium, monochromatic ultraviolet radiation of wavelength 300 nm is shone on the metallic surface of some potassium. Electrons are emitted by the potassium. The fastest-moving electrons are found to have kinetic energy of 2.2 eV.

    a Explain what is meant by the term *monochromatic*.

    b Show that the energy of a single photon of the ultraviolet radiation is 4.1 eV.

    c Explain what is meant by the term *work function*.

    d Calculate the work function of potassium, in eV.

    e Most of the electrons emitted by the potassium have a kinetic energy less than 2.2 eV. Explain why this is so.

15 a Electrons may be said to exhibit wave-like behaviour. Describe briefly one way in which this behaviour may be demonstrated.

    b Atoms may also show wave-like behaviour. Calculate the de Broglie wavelength of an atom whose momentum is 3×10^{-20} kg m s^{-1}.

16 An electron in an atom has an energy of -4.4 eV. It drops to a lower energy level, of energy -7.2 eV. Calculate:

    a the energy of the photon emitted, in J;

    b its frequency.

Appendix 1: Accuracy and errors

Physicists try to make their observations as accurate as possible. Errors in measurements arise in a number of ways and, as an experimentalist, you should try to minimise errors.

Systematic errors

These can arise in a number of ways:

- **Zero error:** e.g. an ammeter that does not read zero when no current is flowing through it. If it reads +0.05 A, all of its readings will be too high. Either correct the meter to read zero, or adjust all readings to take account of the error.
- **Incorrect calibration** of an instrument: e.g. an ammeter that reads zero when no current flows, but all other readings are consistently too low or too high. It may read 9.9 A when 10.0 A is flowing. Again, either correct the meter, or adjust all readings.
- **Incorrect use** of an instrument: e.g. screwing a micrometer too tightly, or viewing a meniscus from an angle. Learn the correct technique for using instruments and apparatus.
- **Human reaction:** e.g. when starting and stopping a stopclock. You may always press the button a fraction of a second after the event.

Systematic errors can be reduced or even eliminated. This increases the **accuracy** of the final result.

Random errors

These often arise as a result of judgements made by the experimenter:

- **Reading from a scale.** You may have to judge where a meter needle is on a scale – what is the nearest scale mark? What fraction of a division is nearest to the needle?
- **Timing a moving object.** When did it start to move? When did it pass the finishing line? You have to judge.

The conditions under which the measurement is made can vary:

- **Equipment** can vary. One trolley may have more friction than another. Two apparently identical resistors may have slightly different values.
- **Samples of materials** may be different. Two lengths of wire from the same reel may have slightly different compositions.
- **Conditions** can vary. Room temperature may change and affect your results.

Some measurements are intrinsically random:

- **Radioactive decay.** If you measure the background radiation in the laboratory for 30 s, you are likely to find slightly different values each time.

Random errors can be reduced, but it is usually impossible to eliminate them entirely. Reducing random errors increases the **precision** of the final result.

Reducing random errors

Here are some ways to reduce random errors.

- **Make multiple measurements,** and find the mean (average). Roughly speaking, taking four measurements reduces the error by half; 100 measurements will divide the error by 10.

- **Plot a graph,** and draw a smooth curve or a straight line through the points.
- **Choose a suitable instrument** to reduce errors of judgement, e.g. using light gates and an electronic timer instead of timing with a stopwatch. You need to think critically about the instrument: does it introduce other sources of error?

Expressing errors

Here are two ways in which the error or uncertainty in a final result can be expressed.

- **Use significant figures:** a calculation may give $R = 127 \, \Omega$. If the errors are small, you may wish to quote this as $130 \, \Omega$; if the errors are large, as $100 \, \Omega$.
- **Use ± errors:** by considering the errors in individual measurements, you may be able to show the degree of uncertainty in the above result. Small error: $R = (127 \pm 2) \, \Omega$; larger error: $R = (130 \pm 10) \, \Omega$.

Using dataloggers

A datalogger can be used to record data from electronic sensors. Sensors can measure many quantities, such as current, pressure and temperature. Their output is a voltage, and this is what the datalogger records.

Advantages of dataloggers include:

- They can record data from several sensors at once.
- They can record data over long periods of time.
- They can record data at very short intervals of time.
- They can make many thousands or millions of records.

Then the data can be printed out and interpreted 'by hand', or computer software can be used to analyse the data, plot graphs and so on. Although dataloggers are enormously useful, they should be approached critically, like any scientific instrument. Sensors may be incorrectly calibrated or incorrectly used; the user may not have chosen the best settings for data collection, so that the pattern in the data does not show up clearly.

Summary

- Think critically about the equipment and methods you use.
- Reduce random errors to increase the precision of your results.
- Reduce systematic errors to increase the accuracy of your results.
- Indicate the extent of error or uncertainty in individual results, and in the final result.

Appendix 2: SI Units

A physical quantity generally consists of a number (its numerical magnitude) and a unit. In science, we use SI units. 'SI' stands for 'Système International d'Unités', or International System of Units. Wherever measurement is important (not just in science), a standardised system of units allows users to be sure that their measurements are consistent with an agreed standard.

Base units

The SI system has seven base units. All other units are defined in terms of these seven units. The first four base units are relevant to the two AS Units covered in this book. The kelvin and the mole appear in A2 physics.

Each base unit is carefully defined, so that people using the SI system can readily check and calibrate their own instruments. The definitions are beyond the scope of this specification.

Unit	Symbol	Unit of ...
metre	m	length
kilogram	kg	mass
second	s	time
ampere	A	electric current
kelvin	K	temperature
mole	mol	amount of substance
candela	cd	luminous intensity

Hint

You can find out more about the SI units, including definitions of the base units, from the website of the National Physical Laboratory: www.npl.co.uk/reference/index.html

Derived units

Velocity is measured in m s^{-1}. This is a derived unit, because it is composed of two base units (m and s). There is no special name for this unit.

Many derived units have special names. (Note that, where the unit is named after a person, the symbol for the unit has a capital letter but the name does not; for example, N = newton.)

Unit	Symbol	Unit of ...	In base units
newton	N	force	kg m s^{-2}
joule	J	energy	kg m^2 s^{-2}
watt	W	power	kg m^2 s^{-3}
hertz	Hz	frequency	s^{-1}
coulomb	C	electric charge	A s
volt	V	potential difference	kg m^2 A^{-1} s^{-3}
ohm	Ω	electric resistance	kg m^2 A^{-2} s^{-3}

There is no need to learn these relationships between derived units and base units. However, it is useful to be able to work them out for yourself, starting from equations which define relevant quantities. For example, 'force' is defined by the equation:

force = mass × acceleration $F = ma$

Its unit, the newton, is therefore equal to the units of mass × acceleration:

$1\,N = 1\,kg \times 1\,m\,s^{-2}$ or $1\,N = 1\,kg\,m\,s^{-2}$

Prefixes

In the SI system, prefixes are used to show multiples and sub-multiples of units. For example 1 mm (1 millimetre) is one-thousandth of a metre. (Note that the kilogram is an odd exception – it already includes a prefix – k – and so multiples such as the megagram are rarely used. Sub-multiples such as grams and milligrams are used.)

As your course progresses, you will come across these prefixes in different contexts. It is important that you become familiar with them, and also that you learn how to use them in calculations.

Multiples

Name	Prefix	Multiple
kilo	k	$1000 = 10^3$
mega	M	10^6
giga	G	10^9
tera	T	10^{12}
peta	P	10^{15}

Sub-multiples

Name	Prefix	Multiple
milli	m	$0.001 = 10^{-3}$
micro	μ	10^{-6}
nano	n	10^{-9}
pico	p	10^{-12}
femto	f	10^{-15}

Hint

Make sure that you know how to use the 'powers of ten' function on your calculator (the 10^x or EXP key).
The EXP key means 'times ten to the power of'.

Appendix 3: Data and formulae for question papers

In examination papers, you will be supplied with a long list of data, formulae and relationships relevant to each unit. **Part 1** below shows the data and equations relevant to Units 1 and 2.

Part 2 shows the formulae and relationships relevant to Units 1 and 2. Note that you need to be familiar with the symbols used in these equations. You should also know the circumstances in which they can be applied.

Part 1: Data and equations supplied in question papers

acceleration of free fall, $g = 9.81$ m s^{-2}
speed of light in a vacuum, $c = 3.00 \times 10^8$ m s^{-1}
elementary charge, $e = 1.60 \times 10^{-19}$ C
Planck constant, $h = 6.63 \times 10^{-34}$ J s
electron rest mass, $m_e = 9.11 \times 10^{-31}$ kg
proton rest mass, $m_p = 1.67 \times 10^{-27}$ kg

electron volt, 1 eV $= 1.60 \times 10^{-19}$ J
1 day $= 8.64 \times 10^4$ s
1 year $\sim 3.16 \times 10^7$ s

circumference of circle $= 2\pi r$
area of circle $= \pi r^2$
curved surface area of cylinder $= 2\pi rh$
volume of cylinder $= \pi r^2 h$
surface area of sphere $= 4\pi r^2$
volume of sphere $= \frac{4}{3}\pi r^3$
Pythagoras' theorem: $a^2 = b^2 + c^2$

> **Hint**
>
> Make sure that you are familiar with these lists of data, formulae and equations, so that you know what is provided on the question papers.

> **Hint**
>
> It is worth remembering that area of a circle $= \frac{\pi d^2}{4}$.

Part 2: Formulae and relationships supplied in question papers

Unit 1: Mechanics

$F_x = F \cos \theta$
$F_y = F \sin \theta$
$a = \dfrac{\Delta v}{\Delta t}$
$v = u + at$
$s = \frac{1}{2}(u + v)t$
$s = ut + \frac{1}{2}at^2$
$s = vt - \frac{1}{2}at^2$
$v^2 = u^2 + 2as$
$F = ma$
$W = mg$
moment $= Fx$
torque $= Fd$
$\rho = M/V$

> **Hint**
>
> Although these formulae are provided in exams, you need to know what they mean and when they can be applied.

$p = F/A$

$W = Fx \cos \theta$

$E_k = \frac{1}{2} mv^2$

$E_p = mgh$

$$\text{efficiency} = \frac{\text{useful energy output}}{\text{total energy input}} \times 100\%$$

$F = kx$

$E = \frac{1}{2} Fx = \frac{1}{2} kx^2$

$\text{stress} = \dfrac{F}{A}$

$\text{strain} = \dfrac{x}{L}$

$\text{Young modulus} = \dfrac{\text{stress}}{\text{strain}}$

Unit 2: Electrons, waves and photons

$\Delta Q = I \Delta t$

$I = Anev$

$W = VQ$

$V = IR$

$R = \dfrac{\rho l}{A}$

$P = VI = I^2 R = \dfrac{V^2}{R}$

$W = VIt$

$\text{e.m.f.} = V + Ir$

$V_{out} = \dfrac{R_2}{R_1 + R_2} \times V_{in}$

$v = f\lambda$

$\lambda = \dfrac{ax}{D}$

$d \sin \theta = n\lambda$

$E = hf = \dfrac{hc}{\lambda}$

$hf = \phi + KE_{max}$

$\lambda = \dfrac{h}{mv}$

Appendix 4: Electrical circuit symbols

You need to be able to recall and use appropriate circuit symbols; you also need to be able to draw and interpret circuit diagrams that include these symbols.

Name of device	Symbol
Junction of conductors (optional dot)	
Conductors crossing (no connection)	
Cell	
Battery of cells	
Open terminals	
Indicator or light source	
Fixed resistor	
Potentiometer (voltage divider)	
Light-dependent resistor (LDR)	
Thermistor	
Ammeter	
Voltmeter	
Semiconductor diode	
Light-emitting diode (LED)	
Switch	

Answers to quick check questions

Unit 1 Mechanics

Module 1 – Motion

Velocity and displacement
1 30 km h⁻¹; 8.3 m s⁻¹; speed varies during the journey
2 200 m s⁻¹
3 40 s
4 Direction changes, so velocity is not constant.
5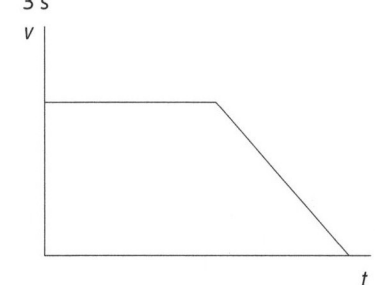

6 9 m s⁻¹

Acceleration
1 4 m s⁻²
2 3 s
3

4 −0.6 m s⁻²; 3750 m

Equations of motion – part 1
1 1.25 m s⁻²; 250 m s⁻¹
2 19.6 m
3 25 m s⁻¹
4 540 m
5 8.1 m s⁻¹
6 9 s; 189 m
7 Eqn 1: m s⁻¹; eqn 2: m; eqn 3: m; eqn 4: m²

Equations of motion – part 2
1 20 m s⁻¹
2 0.5 m s⁻²; 95 m
3 25 km

Using vectors
1 560 km
2 1077 km; 22° E of N
3 6.9 m s⁻²
4 6.6 m s⁻¹; 4.6 m s⁻¹

Gravity and motion
1 44.1 m
2 17.1 m
3 The body's acceleration will decrease as drag increases, and so acceleration is not constant, a requirement for the equations of motion.
4 t will be increased; this will give a reduced value of g.
5 0.72 s; 2.55 m

Module 2 – Forces in action

Force, mass, acceleration
1 vector
2 36 N
3 2 m s⁻² upwards
4 750 kg
5 scalar
6 A

Gravity and weight
1 392 N
2 48.9 kg
3 228 N
4 weight: vector; mass: scalar
5 Velocity decreases until it reaches a slower, steady value.
6 17.4 N; air resistance will increase as it moves faster; resultant force and acceleration will decrease.

Turning effect
1 20 N m; 14.1 N m
2 3 N and 3 N; 15 N m
3 5 N to right
4 600 kg m⁻³; 2 m³
5 150 000 N (= 150 kN)

Car safety
1 16.5 m
2 48 m
3 9 m; 37.5 m; 46.5 m
4 On an icy road, the acceleration when braking will be reduced as there is less friction. This means that, for a given speed, braking distance will be more, and hence stopping distance will be increased.
5 The seat belt must allow the driver to move a small amount during an impact, so that he or she is brought to a halt over an interval of time, rather than instantaneously. This reduces the average force of the impact.

Module 3 – Work and energy

Force, work, energy and power
1 2500 J
2 10 kJ; 4 kJ; 6 kJ
3 1600 J
4 Using $W = Fx$ and $F = ma$, we have 1 J = 1 N m = 1 kg × 1 m s⁻² × 1 m
5 2.5%
6 3000 kJ (= 3 MJ)
7 500 W

Kinetic and potential energy
1 400 J
2 90 000 J
3 200 kJ; 1.96 MJ
4 6 000 000 000 J, or 6×10⁹ J
5 20 J; no energy is lost to air resistance
6 490 500 J; 22.1 m s⁻¹
7 9.8 m s⁻¹

Deforming solids
1 0.2 m; 250 N m⁻¹
2 80 J

3 3 J
4 0.002; 1.6 mm
5 200 GPa; brittle

Unit 2   Electrons, waves and photons

Module 1 – Electric current

Charge and current
1 5 A
2 14 A
3 The charge that flows when a current of 1 A passes for 1 s
4 8 mA (= 0.008 A)
5 6000 C
6 32 A
7 3.1×10^{-3} m s^{-1}

Module 2 – Resistance

p.d. and e.m.f.
1 9 J
2 **a** e.m.f.
   b p.d.
3 60 J
4 230 J
5 2 V
6 5
7 12 V
8 **a** 6.0 V
   b 1.0 V

Resistance
1 5 Ω
2 10 000 V (= 10 kV)
3 $R = 11$ Ω approx.

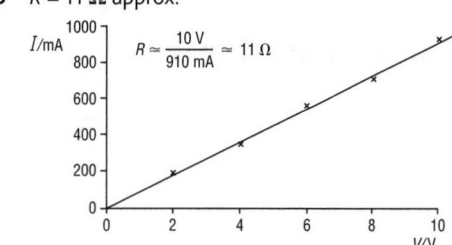

4 6 V; 2 Ω

Resistivity
1 Both wires have same resistance.
2 24 Ω
3 0.08 Ω
4 1.1×10^{-7} Ω m
5 1.2 Ω m^{-1}
6 Metal: increases; semiconductor: decreases

Electrical power
1 450 MJ (= 450 million J, or 450 000 000 J)
2 0.5 W
3 180 J
4 30 W
5 5 A
6 3.6 kWh
7 140 p

Module 3 – D.C. circuits

e.m.f. and internal resistance
1 3.997 A
2 1.55 V; 19.4 Ω
3 4 V
4 160 V
5 **a** 6 V
   b 0.2 A
   c 1 V, 2 V, 3 V; 6 V (= 1 + 2 + 3 V)

Practical circuits
1 2.5 V across each
2 10 Ω
3 18 mA
4 4 V
5

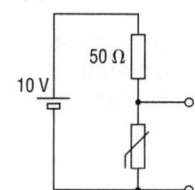

Module 4 – Waves

Wave representations
1 Sound is longitudinal, the others transverse.
2 transverse
3

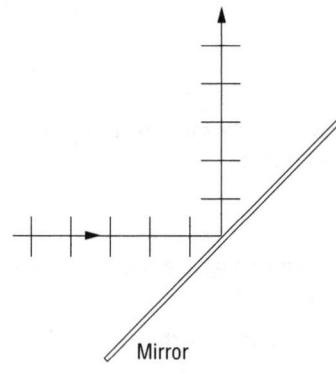

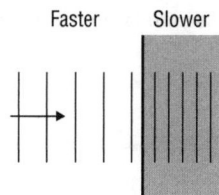

4 wave fronts closer together

Wave quantities
1 p = amplitude = 5 cm; q = wavelength = 4 m
2 0.5 s; 0.5 ms; 2 μs
3 2.5 kHz
4

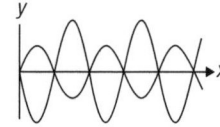

5 half a wavelength = 12 cm
6 90°; $\dfrac{\pi}{2}$ rad
7 133 Hz

Wave speed
1 200
2 60 m
3 45 mm s⁻¹ (= 0.045 m s⁻¹)
4 30 kHz
5 1.5 m

The electromagnetic spectrum
1 7×10^{-7} m (or 700×10^{-9} m)
2 radio, infrared, visible, X-rays
3 UV-C
4 all three
5 500 s

Polarisation
1 Yes – microwaves are electromagnetic waves and thus transverse, so they can be polarised.
2 Sound waves are longitudinal and so cannot be polarised.
3 a The second filter is the same orientation as the first filter.
   b The filters are now crossed, so the light is blocked by the second filter.
4 4
5 10 W m⁻²
6 63.4°

Interference and diffraction
1 single wave of same wavelength, 3 times the amplitude
2 60 cm; 1.5 λ; destructive interference
3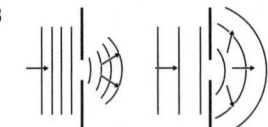

4 Yes; they vibrate up and down with the same frequency because they are driven by the same vibrator.

Interference of light
1 D; a; x; λ
2 Light waves diffract as they pass through the slits – otherwise they would not overlap and interfere.
3 Path difference = (integer + ½) × wavelength.
4 halved
5 555 nm; measurements of very small magnitude are difficult to make, and therefore tend to have errors.
6 6.9°

Superposition and stationary waves
1 λ = 1.2 m
   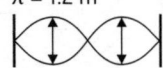
2 3.0 cm
3 Displacements are always equal and opposite.
4 80 cm; 320 m s⁻¹

Module 5 – Quantum physics

Photons
1 3.315×10^{-19} J
2 2.8×10^{-19} J
3 10.5 eV
4 2.07 eV
5 654 nm (6.54×10^{-7} m)
6 9.5×10^{-28} kg m s⁻¹

The photoelectric effect
1 an e.m.f.; from – to + (as in any cell)
2 3.62×10^{14} Hz
3 1.2 eV
4 2.9×10^{5} m s⁻¹

Wave–particle duality
1 slower; larger diameter rings
2 particles
3 2000 eV or 2.0 keV; 3.2×10^{-16} J
4 The electrons must have much higher momentum so that their wavelength is very short, comparable to nuclear dimensions.
5 4.4×10^{-16} m; smaller than the nuclear diameter, so diffraction by the nucleus is possible.
6 6.6×10^{-38} m

Spectra
1 –5.0 eV; –8.0 eV; –12.0 eV
2 absorption; 5.0 eV
3 2.3×10^{15} Hz
4 1.29×10^{-8} m
5 No two energy levels are separated by 4.8 eV.

Answers to end-of-unit questions

Unit 1   Mechanics

Module 1 – Motion

1 a A vector has magnitude and direction, a scalar quantity has only magnitude.

   b vectors: force, velocity, acceleration; scalars: distance, kinetic energy, power

2 a Acceleration = change in velocity/time taken.

   b AB: 1.5 m s^{-2}; BC: 0

   c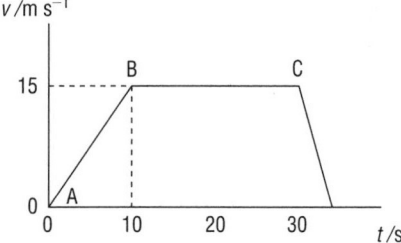

3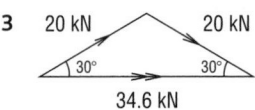

   Resultant force = 34.6 kN

4 a 96 m

   b 22 m s^{-1}

5 a 3.3 m

   b 22.3 m s^{-1} vertically downwards

   c 7.1 m s^{-1} vertically downwards

   d 3.1 s

6 See the experiment described on page 12.

Module 2 – Forces in action

7 a 10 N to left   b 0.25 m s^{-2}

   c 800 kg m^{-3} d 3270 Pa

8 a newton (N)   b 1 N = 1 kg m s^{-2}

9 a Air resistance (drag) decreases as speed decreases.

   b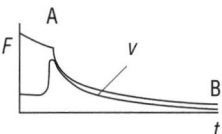

10 a There is a downward pull of 9.81 N on each kg of the mass of an object at the Earth's surface.

   b 90 kg; 342 N

   c 9.81 N kg^{-1} = 9.81 kg m s^{-2} kg^{-1} = 9.81 m s^{-2}

11 a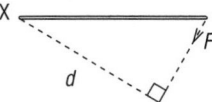

   Moment = $F \times d$

   b 4000 N m

   c $T \cos 50° \times 3$ m = 4000 N m, so

   $T = \dfrac{4000\ \text{N m}}{\cos 50° \times 3\ \text{m}} = 2074$ N

12 a 5 m s^{-2}

   b 100 m

   c The air bag prevents the driver from colliding with the windscreen. As the driver's face hits the air bag, the bag deflates, ensuring that the impact occurs over a greater length of time, so that the force is less.

Module 3 – Work and energy

13 $\Delta E_p = 1.96 \times 10^9$ J; $\Delta E_k = 8.75 \times 10^8$ J

14 a 40 MPa

    b 0.2 (or 20%)

    c 200 MPa

15 a Extension/m

    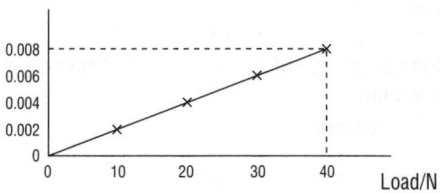

    Spring constant = 5000 N m^{-1}.

    b the load beyond which the spring becomes permanently strained

    c 0.16 J

16 a See graph on page 27.

    b Elastic while straight line; plastic when curved (beyond elastic limit).

    c Elastic: returns to original dimensions when stress removed.

Unit 2   Electrons, waves and photons

Modules 1–3 – Electricity

1 a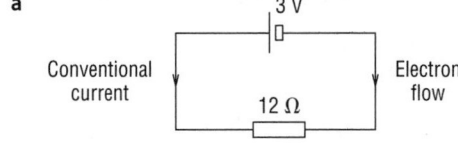

   b 0.25 A; 0.25 C

   c 3 V

   d 0.75 J

2 a $V = \dfrac{W}{Q}$; p.d. = energy transferred per coulomb.

   b 1 V = 1 J C^{-1}

   c W = 1 J; Q = 1 C

3 a in parallel

   b 5 V

   c 1250 Ω

   d increase

   e stay the same

4 a 1.52 Ω

   b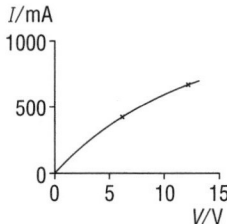

   The I–V graph is not a straight line through the origin, so the copper alloy wire is non-ohmic.

5 a 5.0 V

   b 10.0 V

   c smaller current, so fewer lost volts

6 a 66.7 Ω

   b 3.6 kWh

Module 4 – Waves

7 a 0.12 m

  b increased

8 Metal plates vertical with slit, width a few cm, between them. Generator behind slit. Explore space beyond slit. Look for high and low intensity points.

9 a A bright fringe is formed where two waves, one from each slit, meet and interfere constructively. The path difference between them must be a whole number of wavelengths.

  b 1.3 mm

10 a sound waves

  b light waves and microwaves

11 a Node: amplitude of vibration is zero. Antinode: amplitude is maximum.

Node   Antinode

  b Travelling waves run along string in both directions. Waves reflect at ends, and reflected waves meet and interfere with each other.

12 a Transverse, as displacement perpendicular to velocity.

  b 1.2 m s^{-1}

  c 2 cm

Module 5 – Quantum physics

13 a in free space, or in a vacuum

  b 5.0×10^{-7} m (= 500 nm)

  c visible

14 a single wavelength

  b 4.14 eV

  c the minimum energy needed to remove a conduction electron from the metal

  d 1.94 eV

  e Only the most weakly bound electrons have this KE. Most of the electrons were more tightly bound within the metal.

15 a brief description of electron diffraction – see page 68

  b 2.2×10^{-14} m

16 a 4.5×10^{-19} J

  b 6.8×10^{14} Hz

Index

TROWBRIDGE
LEARNING CENTRE

**TROWBRIDGE
LEARNING CENTRE**